A COMPLETE GUIDE TO
BRITISH MOTHS

A COMPLETE GUIDE TO BRITISH MOTHS

(MACROLEPIDOPTERA)

Their entire life history described and illustrated in colour
from photographs taken in their natural surroundings

...garet Brooks

...ication plates by

...vid Wilson

NATHAN CAPE
LONDON

To my father, John L. Brooks, this work is dedicated. His own fascination with moths began in 1905 when as a young child he reared Garden Tiger moths, and I have always been able to draw on the wealth of knowledge of the Lepidoptera which he has accumulated since then. He has assisted in the fieldwork for this book, provided a steady supply of larval foodplants, patiently advised on all aspects of the work, and drawn all the life cycle diagrams. Without his whole-hearted support and encouragement, this book would have been impossible.

M.B.

My grateful thanks are due to the many people who have helped in the preparation of this book. I must single out Stuart Roberts, who has shared the fieldwork with me from the beginning, and who has devoted so much of his spare time to the project. I am also deeply indebted to Scarsdale Brown, David Carter (British Museum of Natural History), Michael Chalmers-Hunt, Kevin Cook, Philip Grey, Humfrey Halahan, Alec Harmer, Desmond Le Pard, Tony Pickles, Dr Robin Sadler, Mark Spencer, and Paul Waring; to Dr Nigel Webb (Institute of Terrestrial Ecology) who provided so much livestock, read the manuscript, and offered constructive criticism; and to Jim Porter for the photograph of the larva of *Zeuzera pyrina*. Heartfelt thanks also to those who so generously lent precious specimens from their collections for illustration in the identification plates: Bernard Skinner, Barry Goater, David Wilson, Jeffrey and Herbert Findlay, and Peder Skou.

First published 1991
© Margaret Brooks 1991

Jonathan Cape, 20 Vauxhall Bridge Road, London SW1V 2SA

A CIP catalogue record for this book
is available from the British Library

ISBN 0-224-02195-8

Photoset by Rowland Phototypesetting Ltd, Bury St Edmunds, Suffolk
Printed by Butler & Tanner Ltd, Frome and London

Contents

Identification Plates

Introduction

Butterflies are popular, colourful insects, familiar to everyone who visits the countryside, and are regarded with affection by most people. Moths, however, are not so well-loved – there is a widespread misconception that they are all dull brown creatures that chew holes in clothes and carpets. A few of the smaller species do have this unfortunate dietary preference, and a great many moths are brown, but dull and uninteresting they are not.

Moths are often divided into two groups based on details of anatomical structure: 'Macro' – larger moths – and 'Micro' – smaller moths. If considered solely on the basis of size, this division is rather meaningless, as some Macros are smaller than some Micros. This book deals only with those moths normally referred to as Macros, of which over eight hundred species occur in Great Britain. These are divided into seventeen families, most of which are divided again into subfamilies. The main aim of this book is to illustrate the complete life histories of moths, but since dealing with every species in this way would produce a very large and cumbersome volume a total of eighty life cycles has been chosen for detailed coverage, including both representative and non-representative species of every family and every subfamily. Within this framework, species have been selected to give some idea of the tremendous diversity of life styles – for example, the different stages in which overwintering occurs in different species, and the variety of feeding habits of the larvae – most species consume leaves, but others feed on seeds, flowers, roots, the insides of stems, or the solid wood of trees. Each stage of the life cycle is illustrated – the adult moth, showing the natural resting position (often so different from that shown in identification plates), the eggs (where known), the larva, showing any major changes in appearance which take place during this stage, and the pupa. The second section of the book consists of a series of plates illustrating set specimens of all the British Macro moths, to enable the reader to identify any species. Major geographical races are illustrated. The only species omitted from these plates are some which have only been recorded in this country on very few occasions and forms which are extremely limited in their distribution. Variation occurs frequently among moths – more often in some species than in others. These aberrations are not illustrated, as they are so numerous as to require a volume of their own, but mention is made of notable examples under the relevant life histories. The captions of the identification plates provide basic information on the flight periods, distribution, habitat and larval foodplants of each species. Accompanying each life history is a diagram showing the duration of each stage. Maximum durations are given, though these will vary according to locality and climatic conditions.

The names – both English and scientific – used in this book follow *A Recorder's Log Book of British Butterflies and Moths* (1979, revised 1986) by Bradley and Fletcher, and *English Names of Wild Flowers* 2nd Edition (1986) by Dony, Jury and Perring.

Although most moth species are on the wing during spring, summer and early autumn, there is not a single month when moths are not flying – a fact reflected in the English names of a few species: the Winter Moth, the November Moth, the December Moth. In spite of the enormous number of British species, a great deal still remains to be discovered about many of them. Butterflies can be followed and their courtship and egg-laying can be watched. While some moths fly by day, the majority are night-flyers, which makes it extremely difficult to watch them going about their normal business. For several British species, wild larvae have not been observed and oviposition sites and larval foodplants are still unknown.

Knowing more about the life histories and requirements of moths is important if they are to be conserved. Many species are declining through destruction of their habitats, changes in land management and other factors. Further study may help to save more of these diverse, often beautiful, and always fascinating insects.

M.B.

The Biology of Moths

Recognition and Identification

The most reliable feature which may be used to distinguish moths from butterflies is the shape of the antennae. Butterflies' antennae are tipped with a club, whereas those of moths may be any one of a variety of shapes, none of which ends in a club, although in some species the antennae are called clavate, or clubbed, when they are thickened towards the tip (Figure 1). Butterflies are known collectively as Rhopalocera (club horns) and moths as Heterocera (other horns).

Other features often used to distinguish moths from butterflies are:

(i) Butterflies fly by day, whereas moths fly by night.

This is true of the majority of moths, but a few species, for example the Burnets (*Zygaena* spp.) and the Speckled Yellow (*Pseudopanthera macularia*), fly only during the day.

(ii) Butterflies (with one exception, the Dingy Skipper) rest with their wings closed vertically over their backs. Moths rest with their wings laid along the body, the forewings covering the hindwings, or with the wings held out flat against the surface on which the moth is resting.

However, some species of moths, for example the Thorns, rest like butterflies (Plate 1).

(iii) The fore- and hindwings of butterflies are not connected, whereas those of moths are held together in flight in one of two ways:

a) In the more primitive moths such as the Swifts (Hepialidae), the wings are joined by a jugum – a lobe which projects over the base of the hindwing from the inner margin of the forewing.

b) In most other species, a frenulum joins the wings. This consists of bristles (in males there is usually only one bristle, but in females there may be several) at the base of the underside of the hindwing,

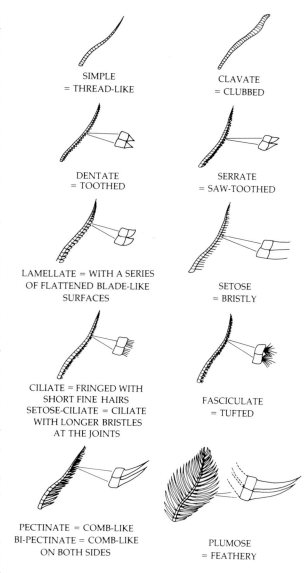

SIMPLE = THREAD-LIKE

CLAVATE = CLUBBED

DENTATE = TOOTHED

SERRATE = SAW-TOOTHED

LAMELLATE = WITH A SERIES OF FLATTENED BLADE-LIKE SURFACES

SETOSE = BRISTLY

CILIATE = FRINGED WITH SHORT FINE HAIRS
SETOSE-CILIATE = CILIATE WITH LONGER BRISTLES AT THE JOINTS

FASCICULATE = TUFTED

PECTINATE = COMB-LIKE
BI-PECTINATE = COMB-LIKE ON BOTH SIDES

PLUMOSE = FEATHERY

Figure 1 Types of Moth Antennae

which interlock with a tuft of stiff hairs or a bristle (the retinaculum) at the base of the underside of the forewing.

Plate I   Resting Attitudes of Moths
(i) Noctuidae
Flame Shoulder *Ochropleura plecta*;
wingspan 28–34 mm

Orange Sallow *Xanthia citrago*; wingspan 32–38 mm

(ii) Geometridae
Riband Wave *Idaea aversata*; wingspan 30–35 mm

Scalloped Hazel *Odontopera bidentata*; wingspan 46–49 mm

Large Thorn *Ennomos autumnaria*;
wingspan 50–62 mm

Moths are divided into groups – families, sub-families and species – according to characteristics of wing shape and venation, and the structure of the genitalia, although when observing moths in the field, only wing characteristics can be seen easily. The plates of set specimens at the end of this book, covering all species likely to be encountered in the British Isles, together with the most widespread subspecies, forms, or geographical races, will assist in identification.

Life Cycle

Moths undergo complete metamorphosis – that is, they pass through four distinct stages in their life cycle: (1) egg (ovum, plural ova); (2) caterpillar (larva, plural larvae); (3) pupa, plural pupae; (4) adult moth (imago, plural imagines). The life cycle may be completed in as little as six weeks, or it may take several years, according to the species.

Egg

The eggshell (chorion) is usually hard, but in some groups (for example Plusiinae) it is rather fragile. It may be smooth, finely pitted, or reticulated (with a net-work pattern), or have a pattern of raised ribs. Moth eggs vary tremendously in their shape and patterns, but basically there are two main types: upright, with the micropyle (the tiny opening through which sperm passes to fertilise the egg) at the top, and often with prominent ribs – such eggs are characteristic of many species of Noctuidae – and horizontal, elongated and somewhat flattened, with the micropyle at one end – for example the eggs of many species of Geometridae (Figure 2).

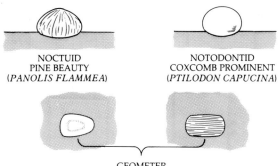

NOCTUID
PINE BEAUTY
(*PANOLIS FLAMMEA*)

NOTODONTID
COXCOMB PROMINENT
(*PTILODON CAPUCINA*)

GEOMETER
COMMON MARBLED CARPET   DUSKY THORN
(*CHLOROCLYSTA TRUNCATA*) (*ENNOMOS FUSCANTARIA*)

Figure 2 Examples of Moth Eggs

The eggs of many species change colour a few days after they are laid, either completely or with the development of coloured blotches. Often a further change occurs immediately before hatching, when the whole egg becomes dark greyish in colour, or a black or brownish spot appears – this is the head of the larva which has become visible through the shell. In some species the eggs appear to collapse just before hatching is due, thus causing alarm to anyone trying to rear them, as such a development can also indicate that an egg is infertile.

According to the species, eggs may be laid singly, in groups of two or three, or in large batches which may consist of several hundred eggs. The choice of site for egg-laying is very great – the eggs may be attached to leaves or twigs, or tucked among buds. The females of some species have ovipositors – tubular structures which they use to insert their eggs into bark crevices or grass sheaths. A few species, such as the Oak Eggar (*Lasiocampa quercus*), the Antler Moth (*Cerapteryx graminis*), and the Swifts (Hepialidae), make no attempt to attach their eggs to anything, but drop them while in flight. Others, such as the Dark Tussock (*Dicallomera fascelina*), lay their eggs in batches, and then conceal them by completely covering them with fluff from the tip of the abdomen.

Larva

Although moth larvae are extremely varied in their shapes and colours (Plate II), they all share the same basic structure – a body made up of head, thorax and abdomen (Figure 3). The head is a horny capsule bearing the short antennae, ocelli (simple eyes), mandibles and spinnerets (the tubes from which silk is extruded). In the wood-feeding species such as the Goat Moth (*Cossus cossus*), Hornet Moth (*Sesia apiformis*), and Lunar Hornet Moth (*S. bembeciformis*), the mandibles are extremely strong. The thorax consists of three segments, to each of which a pair of thoracic, or true, legs are connected, which correspond to the legs of the moth. In some groups, the first seg-

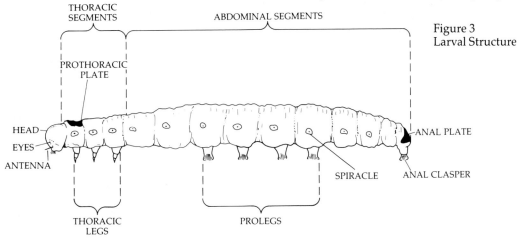

THORACIC
SEGMENTS

ABDOMINAL SEGMENTS

Figure 3
Larval Structure

PROTHORACIC
PLATE

HEAD

EYES

ANTENNA

ANAL PLATE

SPIRACLE   ANAL CLASPER

THORACIC
LEGS

PROLEGS

Plate II Types of Larvae
(i) Noctuidae
Dotted Clay *Xestia baja*; length 40 mm

(ii) Arctiidae
White Ermine *Spilosoma lubricipeda*; length 30 mm

(iii) Geometridae
Dusky Thorn *Ennomos fuscantaria*; length 42 mm

ment, or prothorax, bears a horny piece of armour – the prothoracic plate. The abdomen consists of ten segments, to some of which the prolegs, or false legs, are joined. The number of prolegs varies according to the family or species. Many Noctuids, for example, have five pairs, while most Geometers have only two pairs. Drepanidae (the Hook-tips) and some Notodontidae (the Puss Moth, Kittens and Lobster Moth) have no anal claspers. While many larvae have a smooth skin, others are densely hairy, or bear a few scattered setae (bristles), or have bumps or protuberances on various parts of their bodies. Larvae of the Hawk-moths (Sphingidae) have a horn-like structure at the tail end. The larval skin has only limited elasticity, and so as the larva grows it must periodically shed its skin. The period between each moult is referred to as an instar.

The larvae of some species eat the eggshell immediately after hatching from it. The whole of the larval stage is devoted to eating – it is the only stage in the moth life cycle in which growth takes place. The majority of larvae feed on plants, and each species has its own preferred foodplants. In some cases the larvae are polyphagous – they will eat a wide range of plants – but other species are more particular, and will only feed on one herbaceous plant or tree. Usually it is the leaves which are eaten, but some species use other parts: many of the Pugs (*Eupithecia* spp.) feed on flowers; Noctuids, such as The Campion (*Hadena rivularis*) and Varied Coronet (*H. compta*), feed on the developing seeds. The larvae of the Frosted Orange (*Gor-*

tyna flavago) and several Wainscots feed inside stems, while those of The Butterbur (*Hydraecia petasitis*) live inside roots. Larvae of the Swifts (Hepialidae) are also root feeders, while those of the Leopard Moth (*Zeuzera pyrina*) and Goat Moth (*Cossus cossus*) feed on the living wood inside tree branches and trunks. The family Noctuidae contains a notable carnivore – the Dun-bar (*Cosmia trapezina*) – the larva of which, although it does feed on leaves, seems to prefer the larvae of other species, and is a menace in a breeding cage.

The larval stage of some moth species is extended over two years, particularly in some of those that occur in the north, such as the Northern Dart (*Xestia alpicola alpina*) and the Northern Eggar (*Lasiocampa quercus callunae*). In some wood-feeding species, the larva lives even longer – two to three years in the Leopard Moth, and three to four years in the Goat Moth – probably due to the limited amount of nourishment in their chosen diet.

Pupa

Like the larva, the pupa consists of three parts – the head, thorax and abdomen – which may be seen quite readily (Figure 4). In most groups the shape is very compact, but in some of the more primitive families (Hepialidae, Cossidae, Zygaenidae) the wings, legs and antennae may be partially free from the rest of the body. The proboscis sheath (haustellum) is particularly prominent and well developed in some species of Hawk-moths. The tip of the last abdominal segment often bears spines or minute hooks (the cremaster) to attach the pupa to the inside of a cocoon. Some groups have rows of short backward-pointing spines on the very mobile abdominal segments, so that with the aid of these spines the pupa can work itself out of the cocoon immediately prior to the emergence of the adult.

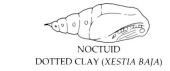

NOCTUID
DOTTED CLAY (*XESTIA BAJA*)

SPHINGID
PRIVET HAWK-MOTH (*SPHINX LIGUSTRI*)

GEOMETER
JULY HIGHFLYER (*HYDRIOMENA FURCATA*)

Figure 4 Pupae

The term 'chrysalis', meaning golden, is often applied to butterfly pupae but is not really relevant to those of moths. The majority of moth pupae are a shade of brown, though there are a few exceptions – some are mainly green, and Catocalinae pupae are covered with a grey or purplish bloom. Most moth pupae are enclosed in a silken cocoon spun by the larva. This may be in a folded leaf or a bark crevice, in litter on the ground, or in an earthen chamber lined with a few silk threads beneath the soil surface. A few species such as the Puss Moth (*Cerura vinula*) form their cocoons on tree bark, mixing particles of chewed wood with the silk to form an extremely hard casing. The Burnets form rather shiny, papery cocoons on grass stems, while several Wainscots pupate inside reed stems. Some Geometers of the subfamily Sterrhinae have girt pupae – supported by a silken girdle round the thorax – which are attached to the undersides of leaves. Hairy larvae such as The Vapourer (*Orgyia antiqua*), Scarce Vapourer (*O. recens*), Pale Tussock (*Calliteara pudibunda*) and Dark Tussock (*Dicallomera fascelina*)

incorporate some of their hairs into the walls of their cocoons. Overwintering pupae normally hatch during the year following pupation, but in some species – for example the Rannoch Sprawler (*Brachionycha nubeculosa*), Belted Beauty (*Lycia zonaria britannica*), Striped Lychnis (*Cucullia lychnitis*) – a few individuals may overwinter up to four times in this stage.

Imago
The body of the imago also consists of head, thorax and abdomen (Figure 5). The head bears the compound eyes, antennae and mouth-parts. Differences in the appearance of the eyes – whether hairy or glabrous (hairless) – can be a help in identifying the family or subfamily to which a species belongs. The antennae can be any of a range of shapes (see Figure 1). The majority of species have a tubular proboscis for sucking up liquid food such as nectar or sap. Several of the Hawk-moths have very long probosces which are inserted into tubular flowers such as honeysuckle and tobacco, enabling the insects to feed while hovering in front of the flowers. The Death's-head Hawk-moth (*Acherontia atropos*) has a short hard proboscis with which it has been known to raid honeycombs. When not feeding, moths keep the proboscis rolled into a neat spiral. In some groups, for example the Saturniidae, the Lymantriidae and the Cossidae, the proboscis is absent or vestigial, and the adults do not feed. On the front of the head are the palpi, which like the antennae are sensory organs; in some groups the shape and size of the palpi are characteristic – the Snouts (Hypeninae), for instance, have comparatively long palpi which project forwards.

The thorax comprises three parts – the prothorax, mesothorax and metathorax – which are often not distinguishable from each other to the casual observer, as they are often densely covered with scales. The thorax bears the legs and wings; one pair of legs is attached to each thoracic segment. Spurs are often present on the mid- and hindlegs, and the males of some species, for example the Fanfoots, have hair pencils (tufts of modified hairs) of scent scales on their legs. These give off a pheromone (scent) attractive to the female during courtship.

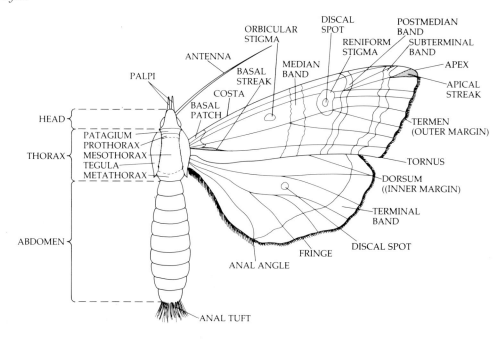

Figure 5 Basic Structure of a Moth

The wings consist of two membranes strengthened by veins running between them. The number and arrangement of these veins vary from one group to another, and form an important means of classification and identification. In the majority of species, the wing membranes are densely covered with minute overlapping scales, each attached by means of a short stalk which fits into a socket in the wing; the Latin name for moths and butterflies – Lepidoptera – means literally 'scale-wings'. Pigments in these scales provide the pattern and ground colour, although in some species 'metallic' colouring is provided by light refraction caused by ridges on the scales. In the family Sesiidae (the Clearwings), large areas of the wings are devoid of scales and therefore transparent. The wing colour and pattern of species which rest with all four wings spread out tends to be similar on both fore- and hindwings, but in those species which rest with only the forewings visible, the hindwings are often brightly coloured. The females of a few species, The Vapourer (*Orgyia antiqua*), the Mottled Umber (*Erannis defoliaria*) and the Winter Moth (*Operophtera brumata*), for instance, have wings either greatly reduced, and therefore useless for flying, or absent altogether.

The abdomen is made up of ten segments, of which the ninth and tenth are modified to form the genitalia. In some very closely related species which are indistinguishable by wing pattern, a microscopic examination of the genitalia provides the only sure means of identification. In some species, notably the Emperor Moth (*Pavonia pavonia*) and those with wingless females, the end of the female's abdomen is furnished with an eversible scent organ with which she produces pheromones to attract a mate – the feathery antennae of the males can detect these scents even from a kilometre away. Males of some species have scent brushes on the abdomen which can be extruded when in the vicinity of a female in order to induce her to mate.

In order for the flight muscles to work well enough for a moth to fly, they must be 'warmed up'. Butterflies do this by opening the wings in sunlight and using them as panels to absorb solar energy. Since the majority of moths fly at night, they cannot use this technique – instead they warm up the flight muscles by vibrating the wings very rapidly for a few minutes before take-off.

Variation

In virtually every species some individuals occur in which the colour or pattern of the wings differs in some way from that of the majority. Moths showing such variation are referred to as aberrations (abs), and each is given a name; for example the variation of the Jersey Tiger (*Euplagia quadripunctaria*) with yellow hindwings is known as ab. *lutescens*. Where a particular variety is common and constant, it is often referred to as a form (f.) – the black variety of the Peppered Moth (*Biston betularia*) is known as f. *carbonaria*.

Geographical variation occurs when the individuals in one particular area differ noticeably from those in another locality, causing them to be classed as a distinct race or subspecies (ssp.). The subspecies of the Ruby Tiger (*Phragmatobia fuliginosa*) which occurs in Scotland, *borealis*, is much darker and less red than ssp. *fuliginosa* which is found in England and Wales.

Species with two generations in a year sometimes exhibit seasonal variation (or Seasonal Dimorphism). Examples are the Purple Thorn (*Selenia tetralunaria*), in which individuals of the spring generation are larger and paler than those of the summer brood, and the Maiden's Blush (*Cyclophora punctaria*), in which the wing markings of the two broods differ.

Sexual Dimorphism is when the males and females of the same species differ noticeably from each other in their appearance. It may include difference in size – in some species the females are very much larger than the males – but is usually regarded as referring to differences in wing pattern or colour. An example is the Muslin Moth (*Diaphora mendica*) – the male is blackish-brown in colour, while the female's wings are white with black spots. Sexual difference is at its most marked in species with wingless females, such as the Belted Beauty (*Lycia zonaria*) and Pale Brindled Beauty (*Apocheima pilosaria*).

Very rarely, individuals are found in which one side of the body and wings is male, the other side female. These are known as bilateral, or halved, gynandromorphs. This is particularly striking when it occurs in such species as The Vapourer (*Orgyia antiqua*) which has a wingless female.

Enemies and Diseases

Of all the offspring of a female moth, very few will develop to adulthood. Predators and diseases will destroy a large proportion at each stage, and unfavourable weather may contribute to many deaths. The destruction of habitats by man and pollution of the moth's natural environment by chemicals also have a tremendous effect.

Predators

These are many and varied. Small birds such as tits will consume the eggs, which may also be sucked dry by predatory insects such as bugs (Hemiptera) and larvae of lacewings (Neuroptera). Larvae may be eaten by birds and beetles, and attacked by carnivorous bugs and slugs. Ants will carry larvae into their nests, as will digger wasps (Hymenoptera – Sphecidae), which paralyse the larvae and then take them back to their nest burrows to form a food larder for their offspring. Although most birds will avoid hairy larvae, the cuckoo is famous for its ability to eat such furry meals without subsequent ill effects. Pupae are eaten by rodents and other small insectivorous animals. Adult moths, like butterflies, are victims of spiders and birds, but also have to contend with the attentions of bats.

Parasites

Moths are affected by two types of parasites – parasitic wasps (Hymenoptera) and parasitic flies (Diptera). Any one of the early stages may be attacked. Some species of wasps lay their eggs inside the moth eggs. The wasp larvae develop and pupate within, and the adult wasp emerges through a hole in the shell. In other species, although the eggs are laid inside the moth eggs, the adult parasites emerge from the fully grown moth larvae. Both wasps and flies also attack the larvae. The parasite larva develops within the body of the host, feeding on non-essential fat bodies and avoiding vital organs. When fully grown, it either emerges from the host's body and pupates outside, or it remains inside the larval skin and pupates there. Other species of wasps inject their eggs into moth pupae, and development takes place within. Adult moths are not subject to attack by parasites.

Diseases

Diseases affecting moths may be bacterial, fungal or viral in origin. Symptoms are most often apparent during the larval stage, when, according to the nature of the causative organism, the larva may go limp, so that it simply hangs helplessly from the vegetation, diarrhoea may develop, or the body may liquefy. Fungus may cause the larva to become stiff; a white mould may develop on it, or the fungus may send out fruiting bodies which then grow from the host's body.

Protective Devices

All stages in the life cycle of a moth are vulnerable to attack by insectivorous predators, and numerous methods of avoiding or minimising predation have evolved (Plate III).

Imago

Adult moths employ a variety of protective devices ranging from concealment to chemical defence. Since the majority of moths fly at night,

Plate III   Protective Devices
(i) Cryptic Coloration
Waved Umber *Menophra abruptaria*; wingspan 36–40 mm

(ii) Industrial Melanism
Peppered Moth *Biston betularia* (*left*
f. *carbonaria*); wingspan 45–60 mm

Oak Beauty *Biston strataria*; wing-span 50–55 mm

(iii) Disruptive coloration
Scorched Carpet *Ligdia adustata*; wingspan 25–30 mm

(iv) Camouflage (imago)
The Lappet *Gastropacha quercifolia*;
wingspan 56–86 mm

Chinese Character *Cilix glaucata*;
wingspan 22–26 mm

Merveille du Jour *Dichonia aprilina*;
wingspan 42–52 mm

Red Sword-grass *Xylena vetusta*;
wingspan 54–62 mm

they have to remain secure during the day. Many species do this by hiding in leaf litter and other debris on the ground, or in the foliage of trees and bushes. The wings may exhibit cryptic or disruptive coloration – that is, they may have colouring and patterning which renders the moth almost invisible when resting in its normal habitat, or be marked with a bold pattern which serves to make the outline of the wings less distinct against the background. Some species such as the Red Underwings (*Catocala* spp.) have cryptically coloured forewings which blend into a bark background, but if the moth is disturbed it displays its bright red hindwings, thus startling a potential predator. The Eyed Hawk-moth (*Smerinthus ocellata*) employs a similar strategy by suddenly flashing the eye-markings on the hindwings. This type of defence is known as flash coloration. A few species, such as the Peppered Moth (*Biston betularia*) have two colour forms, one light, and one dark (melanic). In areas where tree-trunks and fence posts are blackened due to industrial pollution of the atmosphere, the melanic forms are much less conspicuous than the light ones, which fare better on paler backgrounds (Industrial Melanism). Marvellous examples of camouflage are provided by The Lappet (*Gastropacha quercifolia*), which when at rest

(v) Flash coloration
Eyed Hawk-moth *Smerinthus ocellata*; wingspan 75–95 mm

resembles a bunch of dead leaves, and the Chinese Character (*Cilix glaucata*), which gives an excellent imitation of a bird dropping.

Another method of defence employed by moths is mimicry – a close resemblance to another insect which could fight back if attacked. The Broad-bordered and Narrow-bordered Bee Hawk-moths (*Hemaris fuciformis*, *H. tityus*) resemble bees. The Hornet Moth (*Sesia apiformis*), Lunar Hornet Moth (*S. bembeciformis*) and other Clearwings resemble the hornet and other wasps. Certain groups of moths have hearing organs with which they can detect the echolocation sounds emitted by bats – on the approach of a bat, the moth takes rapid avoiding action. Chemical defence is employed by some groups, for example the Burnets (*Zygaena* spp.), whose bright warning colours indicate that they are distasteful and potentially harmful to a predator – their body tissues contain cyanide.

Egg
Many eggs are protected by their coloration, which blends with that of the part of the plant on which they are laid, but the main safeguard for them is the very position in which they are deposited by the female moth – attached to plants, inserted into deep bark crevices, or merely dropped loosely among low-growing vegetation. Some species, for example the March Moth (*Alsophila aescularia*), Yellow-tail (*Euproctis similis*), and Brown-tail (*E. chrysorrhoea*), lay their eggs in batches which are then covered with hairs from the tip of the female's abdomen. In the case of the Brown-tail and Yellow-tail, these hairs are irritant.

Larva
The majority of moth larvae rely on concealment for defence. Many feed only at night, and during the day rest hidden at the base of the foodplant, or in nearby litter, or just below the soil surface. Those feeding on tree leaves often spend the day tucked in a crevice in the bark. Some leaf feeders are green, and blend well with their foodplant, while others rest within a shelter formed by fastening two or more leaves together, or by folding a single leaf over with silk, emerging at night to feed. Larvae of the Geometer family in particular are noted for their astonishing resemblance to twigs – they are frequently known as 'stick' or 'twig' larvae. When resting, they either stretch out along a twig, or rest at an angle to it, holding on with the rear-positioned prolegs. Often their bodies have bumps and wrinkles, exactly like a genuine twig. Some large larvae which normally rest on the underside of twigs exhibit counter-shading; the dorsal surface, which is normally facing downwards, is lighter than the upward-facing ventral surface, therefore rendering the larva much less conspicuous when viewed from below. Larvae of the families Cossidae, Hepialidae and Sesiidae spend their entire lives concealed inside stems, roots or tree trunks. It might be thought that larvae such as those of the Goat Moth (*Cossus cossus*), which feed in tree-trunks, would be safe from predators, but many are dug out by woodpeckers. Birds will also dig out Wainscot larvae from inside reed stems. Larvae such as those of The Lackey (*Malacosoma neustria*) and the Small Eggar (*Eriogaster lanestris*) live gregariously in silken nests, which provide some protection.

(vi) Larval Camouflage

| Swallow-tailed Moth *Ourapteryx sambucaria*; length 60 mm | Purple Thorn *Selenia tetralunaria*; length 35 mm | Beautiful Yellow Underwing *Anarta myrtilli*; length 25 mm |

(vii) 'Fright' Reaction
Lobster Moth *Stauropus fagi*

(viii) Camouflage (pupa)
Sallow Kitten *Furcula furcula*; cocoon – length 25 mm

Some species of larvae exhibit a 'fright' reaction if disturbed. The Elephant Hawk-moth (*Deilephila elpenor*) swells up the front segments to enlarge the 'eye' markings and throw them into prominence. The Puss Moth (*Cerura vinula*) behaves similarly, emphasising the red ring round the head, and in addition it lashes out two whip-like appendages from the anal 'tails' (adapted prolegs). The Lobster Moth (*Stauropus fagi*) unfolds and vibrates its long thoracic legs, thus resembling a spider. The Cinnabar (*Tyria jacobaeae*) larva has warning colours of black and yellow, indicating that it is poisonous. A dense coat of long hairs usually provides protection against birds, with the exception of the cuckoo. In species such as the Brown-tail and Yellow-tail, these hairs are irritant, and can cause a nasty skin rash if handled.

Pupa

These are frequently concealed below the surface of the ground in an earthen chamber or cocoon. Above ground they are usually well hidden – in bark crevices, between spun leaves, and often in cocoons. The Puss and Kitten moths are noted for their incredibly tough cocoons of silk and chewed wood, which blend beautifully with the bark to which they are attached. Pupae developing from larvae that bear irritating hairs often bear such hairs themselves, and the silk of their cocoons is mixed with the larval hairs. The pupa of The Magpie (*Abraxas grossulariata*) is formed in a rather transparent cocoon, but has the warning colours of black and yellow, indicating that it is distasteful to predators.

Migration

The majority of moth species which occur in Great Britain are resident, and maintain their population successfully from one year to the next. Some species, however, have migrated here. Most of these have travelled northwards from North Africa and other countries bordering the Mediterranean, but a few, such as the Scarce Arches (*Luperina zollikoferi*), come from Central Europe, while the Clifden Nonpareil (*Catocala fraxini*) comes from Northern Europe. The migrant species which reach Britain may be divided into five categories:

(i)   Species which come every year and reinforce the resident population, for example the Large Yellow Underwing (*Noctua pronuba*), and the Angle Shades (*Phlogophora meticulosa*).

(ii) Species which come every year and breed successfully, for example the Silver Y (*Autographa gamma*), and Pearly Underwing (*Peridroma saucia*).

(iii)   Species which do not necessarily come every year – some such as The Vestal (*Rhodometra sacraria*) may occasionally be numerous, while others, such as the Oleander Hawk-moth (*Daphnis nerii*), Slender Burnished Brass (*Diachrysia orichalcea*), are scarce and usually recorded in small numbers.

(iv)   Species which came to Britain, became temporarily established, then subsequently died out, for instance the Black V moth (*Arctornis l-nigrum*).

(v)   Species which migrated to Britain and have become established as resident species, such as the Golden Plusia (*Polychrysia moneta*) and Blair's Shoulder-knot (*Lithophane leautieri hesperica*).

The factors governing migration are not yet fully understood. In most cases it seems to be instinctive, although sometimes it may be triggered by conditions prevailing in the usual habitat, such as shortage of the larval foodplant. The success of migration depends on many factors, including the wind direction and other weather conditions both at the starting point and along the route of the migration. Greatest numbers of immigrant moths are recorded in Britain between May and October.

Injurious Species

The larvae of quite a few species of moths can be classed as injurious because they consume and therefore damage portions of plants or trees which are useful to man for one reason or another. The damage caused is very noticeable in the garden. Cutworms (the larvae of several species of Noctuidae) live in the soil and bite through the stems of seedlings and small plants, which then collapse. Hepialid larvae such as the Common Swift (*Hepialus lupulinus*) attack roots. Leaf-feeders found in gardens include the Cabbage Moth (*Mamestra brassicae*), whose larvae bore deep inside cabbages and cauliflowers, and the Elephant Hawk-moth (*Deilephila elpenor*), which can defoli-ate a fuchsia very efficiently. The Golden Plusia (*Polychrysia moneta*) larva nibbles the developing flower spikes of delphiniums.

In orchards, Winter Moths (*Operophtera brumata*) and Lackey moths (*Malacosoma neustria*) feed on leaves of fruit trees, while Leopard Moths (*Zeuzera pyrina*) feed within the branches. Upland pastures are sometimes denuded by Antler Moth (*Cerapteryx graminis*) larvae, while cereal crops can suffer from Common Rustic (*Mesapamea secalis*) larvae which feed within the stems. Pine plantations can be damaged by the Pine Beauty (*Panolis flammea*).

Habitats

While some species of moths may be found in virtually any type of habitat, from sea-cliffs to mountainsides, others are more selective, and for various reasons – such as climate, or the presence of a particular larval foodplant – are confined to certain localities. The main types of habitat to be found in the British Isles are here summarised, together with a few examples of species typical of each.

Woodland
(i) *Broad-leaved Woodland*   This is probably the habitat most favoured by moths, as it is virtually three habitats in one, arranged in layers. At the highest level are the trees, next are the shrubs, bushes and climbers, and at ground level is a layer of grasses and other low-growing plants. Woodland with mixed broad-leaved trees provides the richest source of moths, but a monoculture has its

own species – for example a beechwood will support the Clay Triple-lines (*Cyclophora linearia*) and the Barred Hook-tip (*Drepana cultraria*). Other moths to be found within broad-leaved woods include the Broad-bordered Bee Hawk-moth (*Hemaris fuciformis*) and the Early Grey (*Xylocampa areola*), for which honeysuckle is the larval foodplant, and the Speckled Yellow (*Pseudopanthera macularia*), which feeds on Wood Sage.

(ii) *Coniferous Woodland* Fewer species are to be found in this habitat, although there are still several, including the Pine Hawk-moth (*Hyloicus pinastri*), Bordered White (*Bupalus piniaria*), Barred Red (*Hylaea fasciaria*) and Pine Beauty (*Panolis flammea*).

Heathland and Moorland

These are both open areas whose vegetation consists mainly of heathers. The term heathland is usually applied to low-lying areas, while moorland generally refers to similar areas at higher altitude and mainly in northern Britain. Many species are present in both habitats, their larvae feeding on heathers, or on other vegetation such as bilberry or bog myrtle. Examples are the Common Heath (*Ematurga atomaria*), The Anomalous (*Stilbia anomala*), the Heath Rustic (*Xestia agathina*) and the Powdered Quaker (*Orthosia gracilis*). The wetter areas of heathland and moorland support such species as the Silver Hook (*Eustrotia uncula*), Marsh Oblique-barred (*Hypenodes humidalis*) and Purple-bordered Gold (*Idaea muricata*).

Grassland and Downland

Natural grassland is more commonly found in northern Britain – in the south much has been altered by farming and changes in grazing patterns. Where chalk downland occurs, the rich flora provides a wide range of foodplants for species such as the Foresters (*Adscita* spp.), the Chalk Carpet (*Scotopteryx bipunctaria cretata*) and the Striped Lychnis (*Cucullia lychnitis*). Grassland supports various species of Wainscots, the Antler Moth (*Cerapteryx graminis*), the Common Rustic (*Mesapamea secalis*) and many others. Bushy areas containing hawthorns, buckthorns and other shrubs are favourable localities for many species including the Green-brindled Crescent (*Allophyes*

oxyacanthae), Mottled Umber (*Erannis defoliaria*), and Dotted Border (*Agriopis marginaria*).

Fens and Marshes

The vegetation in these habitats consists mainly of reeds, bulrush, and a few trees such as sallow, willow and alder. Reed-beds are the home of several species of Wainscot including the Fen Wainscot (*Arenostola phragmitidis*) and the Twin-spotted Wainscot (*Archanara geminipuncta*). Bulrush is the foodplant of the Bulrush Wainscot (*Nonagria typhae*) and Webb's Wainscot (*Archanara sparganii*). Sallows and willows in marshy places can harbour the Lunar Hornet Moth (*Sesia bembeciformis*), while on alder can be found the Alder Kitten (*Furcula bicuspis*) and Blue-bordered Carpet (*Plemyria rubiginata*).

Coastal Areas

These may be sub-divided into four separate habitats, each of which, where vegetation occurs, can support moths.

(i) *Sand Dunes* Plants growing in the dune slacks provide larval food for such species as the Belted Beauty (*Lycia zonaria*), Coast Dart (*Euxoa cursoria*) and Sand Dart (*Agrotis ripae*).

(ii) *Shingle Beaches* Significant amounts of vegetation may be found on a few extensive areas of shingle beach, and these support the Dew Moth (*Setina irrorella*) and Toadflax Brocade (*Calophasia lunula*).

(iii) *Cliffs* These largely inaccessible habitats provide a safe refuge for a few species, including the Portland Ribbon Wave (*Idaea degeneraria*), Beautiful Gothic (*Leucochlaena oditis*) and Thrift Clearwing (*Bembecia muscaeformis*).

(iv) *Saltmarsh* Specialised plants such as saltmarsh grasses and sea-wormwood provide larval food for such species as the Crescent-striped (*Apamea oblonga*) and the Essex Emerald (*Thetidia smaragdaria*).

Uplands

Mountain areas of Britain provide a mainly cool and wet habitat with vegetation consisting of bilberry, heather, rushes, and grasses such as mat-grass. Species found in these habitats include the Black Mountain Moth (*Psodos coracina*), Northern Dart (*Xestia alpicola alpina*), Ashworth's Rustic (*X. ashworthii*), and Broad-bordered White Underwing (*Anarta melanopa*).

Gardens

Gardens can boast a comprehensive selection of species, the larvae of which feed on both weeds and cultivated plants. Their attentions to the latter cause gardeners to regard them as pests, and reference to several of these species has already been made in the section on injurious species, although perhaps it is worth mentioning that some of these also consume wild plants which are considered weeds in this particular habitat.

Collecting

The days of collecting long series of specimens, even of lesser-known species, are no longer with us – indeed in some circles any scale of collecting is frowned upon. However, the serious study of moths does require the formation of a small reference collection, as in some groups the species cannot be identified correctly without examining the genitalia. Collectors should familiarise themselves with the Code for Insect Collecting drawn up by the Joint Committee for the Conservation of British Insects, and abide by its recommendations. Those which apply to the collecting of moths may be summarised thus:

No more specimens than are strictly required for any purpose should be killed.

Insects should not be killed if the object is to 'look them over' for aberrations or other purposes; they should be examined alive and released where they were captured.

The same species should not be taken in numbers year after year from the same locality.

Consideration should be given to photography as an alternative to collecting.

Species listed as rare and endangered should be collected with the greatest restraint – a pair of specimens should be sufficient; those species in the greatest danger should not be collected at all.

Specimens of distinct local forms should be collected with restraint.

The 'catch' at light, particularly in a trap, should not be killed casually for subsequent examination.

Live trapping, for instance in traps filled with egg-trays, is the preferred method of collecting. Anaesthetics are harmful and should not be used.

After examination the insects should be kept in cool, shady conditions and released away from the trap site at dusk.

If a trap is found to be catching rare or local species unnecessarily it should be resited.

Traps and lights should be sited with care so as not to annoy neighbours or cause confusion.

Breeding from a fertilised female or from a pairing in captivity is preferable to taking a series of specimens in the field.

Unwanted insects which have been reared should be released in the original locality.

Never collect more larvae or other livestock than can be supported by the available supply of foodplant.

The Committee also recommend that permission be sought from the owner before collecting on private land, and that a list of species obtained be submitted to the owner if required. Damage to the environment should be avoided as much as possible. 'Beating' trees and bushes for larvae should be done with care to avoid breaking off twigs and leaves. 'Sugar' should not be applied so that it renders tree-trunks and other vegetation unnecessarily unsightly.

Under the Wildlife and Countryside Act 1981, the following species are protected, and it is illegal to collect or interfere with any stage or its habitat:

Barberry Carpet – *Pareulype berberata*

Black-veined – *Siona lineata*
Essex Emerald – *Thetidia smaragdaria*
New Forest Burnet – *Zygaena viciae*
Reddish Buff – *Acosmetia caliginosa*
Viper's Bugloss – *Hadena irregularis*

Study

To conduct a survey of the moths in any particular habitat, it is necessary to make regular observations of adult moths throughout the year, and also to search for early stages. The observation of day-flying moths presents few problems, but those species which fly at night require a different approach – one which makes use of the attraction of moths to light. Quite large numbers of moths will often come to the window of a lighted room, or to a hurricane lamp outdoors, but the best attractant is a source of ultra-violet light. Several types of moth trap which employ this principle are available commercially. The most popular models are:

(i) *The Heath Trap*
     A lightweight collapsible metal container with an actinic tube, which will operate from a 12 volt car battery.

(ii) *The Robinson Trap*
     A large circular drum with a powerful mercury vapour lamp, which operates from a 240 volt mains supply or a portable generator.

Both these traps are designed with a system of vanes which deflect moths approaching the lamp down into a container below, which should be packed with papier mâché egg trays. The moths will settle among the trays, and can be sorted the next morning. The Heath trap and 12 volt battery has the advantage of being very portable, and can therefore be taken to remote sites. The Robinson trap is much more efficient in its power to attract moths, but, even with a portable generator, is much more difficult to transport, especially over rough ground. If taken into the countryside, it should be borne in mind that the site should be chosen carefully – a lamp visible from a road may cause a traffic hazard. A white sheet spread on the ground beneath the trap makes it easier to see species which come to the vicinity of the trap but do not go inside. Warm, cloudy, still, slightly damp nights yield the best selection of species. Even an expedition with a hand torch can prove very rewarding, particularly if visiting flowering sallows in the spring when large numbers of moths may be seen feeding at the flowers. Over-ripe blackberries and ivy blossom are attractive to moths in the autumn.

Sugaring

The 'sugar' used for this technique is a mixture of Barbados sugar, black treacle and brown ale in the proportions 4:2:1. These ingredients are brought gently to the boil, simmered for about ten minutes, and then allowed to cool, being stirred occasionally. Just before use a little rum is mixed in. The 'sugar' is applied with a stiff paint brush at dusk, painting a vertical stripe about an inch wide and a foot long on a series of tree trunks or fence posts, choosing a fairly straight route which will be easy to follow after dark. The 'line' is then visited at frequent intervals until about midnight. Moths that are drawn to sugar are generally Noctuidae; often species which do not come to light, such as Old Lady (*Mormo maura*), can be attracted in this way. As with light trapping, a warm, still, humid night yields best results.

Assembling

In certain species a freshly emerged female will attract males from considerable distances. If the female is taken in a net-covered container to a suitable habitat immediately after emergence – usually during the morning – she will begin 'calling'. She extrudes a scent organ from the tip of her abdomen which gives off a powerful pheromone. This can be detected by the males, and they then come to her, often in considerable numbers. Species with which this technique may be used include the Emperor Moth (*Pavonia pavonia*), the Kentish Glory (*Endromis versicolora*), The Vapourer (*Orgyia antiqua*), the Scarce Vapourer (*O. recens*), and some Lasiocampidae.

Searching for early stages

This is another way of determining the presence of a species in a particular habitat, and of finding subjects for observation and photography.

Egg
This is not the easiest stage to find, but careful hunting may sometimes be rewarded. If a particular species is the object, then a search of the known larval foodplants at the appropriate time is often successful.

Larva
Examination of the foodplant may reveal signs of feeding, and if the larva feeds only at night then a return after dark with a torch will often produce results. Two other techniques for finding larvae are:
(i) *Sweeping* This is a particularly useful method when searching for species feeding on grasses and other low-growing plants. A stout net mounted on a strong frame with a short, strong handle is swept from side to side as the bearer walks through the herbage, so that any larvae are swept into the open mouth of the net. As wear and tear on such nets can be severe, it is advisable to use dense, strong material for the bag, and to reinforce the rim with even tougher material such as carpet webbing. When sweeping at night, a light mounted on a head-band is invaluable, as it leaves the hands free to cope with the sweep-net and larvae. Sweeping wet vegetation is not advised – both net and user rapidly become thoroughly soaked, and larvae may suffer.
(ii) *Beating* This method is excellent for obtaining larvae feeding on shrubs or trees. A sheet is spread on the ground beneath the branches, or a beating tray, consisting of cloth stretched over a wooden frame with a handle, is held under them. The branches are then jarred sharply with a stout stick, causing larvae to fall on to the tray or sheet. Care should be taken not to damage the tree or shrub, and repeated bashing is not usually productive – if the larva is not dislodged by the first couple of taps, it will only hang on tighter. Beating is not recommended in wet or windy conditions.

Pupa

These may sometimes be found by searching in bark crevices or between spun leaves, or by digging for them. The latter method is usually employed during the winter. Isolated trees such as oak and poplar are the best source of pupae. Choose a tree which has 'buttress' roots and plenty of grass growing round the base. Carefully pull away the grass from the roots – many pupae can be found there. Then carefully dig between the roots with a trowel – pupae are usually close to the roots and the soil surface. Afterwards be sure to replace soil and surface vegetation before leaving.

Breeding

One of the most fascinating and rewarding aspects of the study of moths is captive breeding. Much can be learned about moths at each stage of the life cycle, and these are also easily available for photography. By protecting the early stages from predators and parasites, a high proportion can be reared to maturity, and the moths released in the habitat from which the original stock was obtained, thus aiding conservation. The golden rule for success is to keep each stage in conditions as natural as possible. Growing foodplant should be provided wherever possible. This requires forward planning, as it is prudent to have the plants well established before adding eggs or larvae, otherwise there is the risk of a newly-potted plant keeling over together with its livestock. Plants can be covered with nylon netting stretched over wire hoops, the ends of which are pushed into the soil in the pot. The netting should be secured below the rim of the pot with string. Small pots can alternatively be placed in wood-framed cages covered with similar net. Rot-proof and parasite-proof nylon netting or ready-made cages can be obtained from various entomological dealers. Where it is impossible or impractical to provide growing foodplant, cut stems or twigs can be used. These should be stood in a narrow-necked container of water with cotton wool packed round them to prevent larval drownings. When introducing fresh food – and it is very important to ensure that this is always available – larvae resting on the original foodplant should not be transferred by hand. The new plant should be placed beside the old so that the leaves are touching. The larvae can transfer themselves to the fresh leaves. The floors of cages should be covered with kitchen tissues to catch the frass (larval faeces), and these tissues should be changed daily – if frass is allowed to collect, it will go mouldy and cause disease. Pots and cages should be kept outdoors in a sheltered spot with partial shade, and some sort of covering to protect against the heaviest rain.

Many species of moths require soil in which to pupate, while the larvae of some spend the day beneath the surface of the soil, emerging at night to feed. With growing foodplant this presents no problems, but if using cut foodplant the container should be standing in a tray of sterile potting soil. Some dead leaves, carefully sorted to remove any predators, should be sprinkled over the soil surface for those species which pupate in surface litter, and to provide a hibernation site for some species of overwintering larvae.

Overcrowding must be avoided – having to keep up a copious supply of foodplant is very hard work for the breeder, and crowded conditions can quickly lead to outbreaks of disease. Some larvae, such as The Dun-bar (*Cosmia trapezina*) and The Satellite (*Eupsilia transversa*), are carnivorous, and it is wise to become familiar with these quickly.

In the section dealing with the life histories, any special requirements are given in the text relating to the species concerned.

THE LIFE HISTORIES

The seventeen families of British Macro moths are listed here, together with their special characteristics. Then follow eighty complete life histories, illustrating representative and non-representative members of each family and subfamily.

HEPIALIDAE (Swifts)

5 species.

Small to medium-sized moths with long wings and very short antennae. Venation of forewings virtually identical to that of hindwings; eyes glabrous; frenulum absent; proboscis undeveloped, so adults do not feed. Members of this family are known as 'Swifts' because of their swift, powerful flight. Night-flyers.

Egg Oval or nearly spherical; smooth. Dropped by female while in flight.

Larva Long, cylindrical; usually whitish; five pairs of prolegs. Subterranean. Feed on roots.

Pupa Long, cylindrical; cremaster absent; abdominal segments have transverse rows of short spines. Subterranean.

COSSIDAE (Leopards and Goat Moth)

3 species.

Medium-sized to large moths. Eyes glabrous; frenulum present; proboscis very short or absent; ovipositor present in females. Night-flyers.

Egg Oval. Laid singly or in small batches.

Larva Horny prothoracic plate present; five pairs of prolegs. Feed internally in trees or stems.

Pupa Abdomen has rows of short spines; head has projecting 'beak'.

2 subfamilies:

ZEUZERINAE (Leopards)
2 species.
Antennae of male pectinate on basal half.

COSSINAE (Goat Moth)
1 species.
Antennae of male pectinate for whole length.

ZYGAENIDAE (Foresters and Burnets)

10 species.

Small to medium-sized moths. Bright warning colours indicate that they are distasteful to predators – all stages contain toxic substances. Eyes glabrous; frenulum present; proboscis well developed; antennae clavate, weakly dentate, or bipectinate. Day-flying. Live in colonies.

Egg Flattened. Laid in batches.

Larva Slug-like; retractile head; five pairs of prolegs.

Pupa Abdominal segments have transverse rows of spines. In cocoon, above ground.

2 subfamilies:

PROCRIDINAE (Foresters)
3 species.

Forewings and bodies metallic green, blue-green or yellowish-green; antennae of males bipectinate, those of females weakly dentate. Young larvae 'mine' leaves. Cocoons thin, semi-transparent, at base of foodplant.

ZYGAENINAE (Burnets)
7 species.
Forewings metallic greenish-black with red spots or streaks; hindwings red; bodies black; antennae clavate. Larvae may overwinter twice. In papery cocoons on stems.

LIMACODIDAE (The Festoon and The Triangle)

2 species.

Small moths. Eyes glabrous; frenulum present; proboscis rudimentary. Fly mainly at night. Associated with wooded areas.

Egg Flattened ovoid; nearly transparent.

Larva Slug-like; retractile head; thoracic legs very small; prolegs absent, replaced by suckers. Slug-like appearance of larva gives family its name, derived from *Limax*, meaning a slug.

Pupa Short; dumpy; legs and antennae free. In oval silken cocoons. Adult moth emerges from one end of cocoon, which is opened like hinged lid.

SESIIDAE (Clearwings)

15 species.

Small to medium-sized moths. Eyes glabrous; frenulum present, and wings also coupled by folded hooked margins; most of fore- and hindwing surfaces free of scales and transparent. Day-flying. Resemble wasps or hornets.

Egg Flattened ovoid; reddish-brown to blackish; very fine reticulation.

Larva Maggot-like; five pairs of prolegs. Live and feed in trunks, twigs or roots of trees and shrubs, or in crowns or roots of some low-growing plants.

Pupa Cylindrical; head has frontal 'beak' for rupturing cocoon and exit from larval tunnel; abdomen has transverse rows of short spines. After emergence of the adult moth, the empty pupa case protrudes from the exit hole.

2 subfamilies:

SESIINAE (Hornets)
2 species.
Moths resemble hornets. Proboscis reduced.

PARANTHRENINAE (Clearwings)
13 species.
Moths resemble wasps. Proboscis well developed; abdomen with expandable anal tuft.

LASIOCAMPIDAE (Eggars, Lackeys and Lappets)

11 species.

Medium-sized to large moths. Frenulum absent; proboscis either rudimentary or absent; antennae of males strongly bipectinate. Night-flying, except for two species where males fly by day.

Egg Generally oval, often slightly flattened on the upper surface.

Larva Hairy (in some species the hairs may be irritant to the skin); five pairs of prolegs. Some species live communally in webs.

Pupa In cocoons either on the foodplant or on the surface of the ground. The very tough, egg-shaped cocoons of some species gave rise to the name 'Eggars'.

SATURNIIDAE (Emperor Moth)

1 species.

Large moth. Eyes glabrous; proboscis undeveloped; frenulum absent; antennae of male strongly pectinate; each wing has 'eye-spot' with hyaline centre. Male flies by day, female at night. The only British representative of a large family, the 'Silk moths' – numerous in the tropics. 'Saturniidae' is derived from the resemblance of the transparent ringed eye-spots to the planet Saturn.

Egg Roundish-oval. Laid in batches round stems or twigs.

Larva When fully grown, green with tubercles bearing tufts of bristles; five pairs of prolegs.

Pupa In a tough, flask-shaped cocoon in low herbage.

ENDROMIDAE (Kentish Glory)

1 species.

Large moth. Females larger than males. Eyes glabrous; proboscis undeveloped; frenulum absent. Males day-flying.

Egg Roundish-oval; slightly flattened. Laid in rows on twigs.

Larva Body tapers to head; stouter behind with penultimate segment humped; five pairs of prolegs.

Pupa In cocoon, on surface of ground.

DREPANIDAE (Hook-tips)

7 species.

Small to medium-sized moths. Eyes glabrous; frenulum present; proboscis vestigial; tips of forewings in all but one species characteristically hooked. Fly mainly at night.

Egg Roundish-oval. Laid on leaves.

Larva Often humped on dorsal surface; four pairs of prolegs; anal claspers absent; last segment tapered and pointed.

Pupa In thin cocoons spun between leaves, or in a folded leaf of the foodplant.

THYATIRIDAE (Lutestrings)

9 species.

Medium-sized moths. Proboscis well developed; frenulum present. Fly at night.

Egg Mainly oval; often ribbed.

Larva Five pairs of prolegs. Feed mainly at night, resting by day among spun leaves.

Pupa Cocoons made of only a few threads, in most species constructed in debris on surface of ground.

GEOMETRIDAE (Geometers)

295 species.

Small to medium-sized moths. Proboscis usually developed; frenulum present; wings large in proportion to slender bodies; wingless females in some species; antennae in female simple. Majority fly at night. Flight not strong.

Egg Usually flattened oval.

Larva Very variable. Known as 'loopers' because of their arching gait. Most have only two pairs of prolegs; often closely resemble twigs.

Pupa Mostly slim. Either below the surface of the ground or in cocoons on the foodplant.

6 subfamilies:

ARCHIEARINAE (Orange Underwings)
2 species.
Eyes glabrous. Day-flying. First three pairs of larval prolegs reduced to stumps.

OENOCHROMINAE (March Moth)
1 species.
Proboscis short; wings of male broad; female wingless with large anal tuft. Larva has two pairs of functional prolegs, and one pair vestigial.

GEOMETRINAE (Emeralds)
10 species.
Proboscis developed; wings of all species except one are green, but the pigment is unstable and fades quickly. Night-flyers. Larvae have notched crown of head. Pupae green or light in colour, contained in thin cocoons.

STERRHINAE (Waves)
38 species (1 presumed extinct in GB).
Proboscis developed. Mainly night-flying, but several species become active around dusk. Larvae slender; a few species have notched heads. Pupae often girt.

LARENTIINAE (Carpets, Pugs and Others)
161 species (1 presumed extinct in GB).
Proboscis developed. Pupae usually below surface of ground.

ENNOMINAE (Thorns, Beauties and Others)
83 species (2 presumed extinct in GB).
Proboscis usually developed. Pupae either below surface of ground, or in slight cocoon above it.

SPHINGIDAE (Hawk-moths)

17 species.

Medium-sized to large moths. Eyes glabrous; frenulum present; proboscis well developed; antennae short, thickened, tapering to tip, which is sometimes hooked. Powerful flight. Feed while hovering in front of flowers.

Egg Rounded, greenish. Usually laid singly on leaves of the foodplant.

Larva Five pairs of prolegs; horn on eighth abdominal segment, reduced in some species; some species with eye-spots on thoracic segments. The defensive attitude, with the head drawn back into the raised hunched thoracic segments, thus resembling the attitude of the Sphinx, has given this family its name.

Pupa Haustellum often enlarged or curved. Either in thin cocoons on the surface, or below ground level.

2 subfamilies:

> SPHINGINAE
> 7 species.
> Large moths. Night-flying.

> MACROGLOSSINAE
> 10 species.
> Medium-sized to large moths. Three species are day-flying. Two species have mainly transparent wings.

NOTODONTIDAE (Prominents and Others)

26 species.

Medium-sized moths. Eyes usually glabrous; proboscis not developed; many species have a tuft of scales on the hind margin of the forewing which projects when the moth is at rest – hence the name 'Prominents'. Fly at night.

Egg Hemispherical. Usually deposited in groups of two or three.

Larva Very variable. Some smooth, others with dorsal humps; five pairs of prolegs, except in the Puss Moth, Kittens and Lobster, where the anal pair are modified into tail-like appendages. Several species rest with both the front and rear portions of the body raised.

Pupa Either in silken cocoons beneath the surface of the ground, or in very tough cocoons of silk mixed with chewed wood on the trunk of a tree.

LYMANTRIIDAE (Tussocks and Others)

11 species (1 presumed extinct in GB).

Medium-sized moths. Proboscis undeveloped; male antennae strongly pectinated; in some species females are wingless, and in others they are larger than males; female often with anal hair tuft. Males of some species fly by day.

Egg Smooth, rounded. Often in batches covered with hairs from anal tuft of female.

Larva Hairy; often brightly coloured; some with hair 'pencils' and tufts (tussocks) of hair on the dorsal surface of some abdominal segments; five pairs of prolegs. In some species the hairs are urticating, and handling them may cause a painful skin rash.

Pupa Hairy. In cocoons of silk mixed with larval hairs, above ground.

ARCTIIDAE (Footmen and Tigers)

32 species.

Small to large moths. Eyes glabrous. Some species toxic to predators. Most fly at night.

Egg Hemispherical. Usually laid in neat batches.

Larva Usually covered with tufts of hairs; five pairs of prolegs.

Pupa In cocoons of silk mixed with larval hairs, above ground.

2 subfamilies:

> LITHOSIINAE (Footmen)
> 17 species.

Small to medium-sized moths. Most species have long slender forewings. Night-flyers. Larvae feed on lichens.

ARCTIINAE (Tiger moths)
15 species.
Medium-sized to large moths. Often brightly coloured; proboscis often undeveloped. Some day-flying. Very hairy larvae – known as 'Woolly Bears' – feed on the leaves of herbaceous plants.

NOLIDAE (Small Arches)

5 species.

Small moths. Proboscis developed; forewings have small tufts of raised scales in the area of the cell. Night-flying.

Egg Often ribbed. Laid on leaves.

Larva Body has tufts of short hairs; four pairs of prolegs.

Pupa In tough boat-shaped cocoons on twigs or stems.

NOCTUIDAE (Noctuids)

375 species.

Small to large moths. Many species dull brown, but some brightly coloured. Proboscis usually developed; frenulum present. Mostly night-flyers.

Egg Dome-shaped and ribbed, or flattened.

Larva Mostly night-feeders that hide during day. Some species injurious to crops.

Pupa Usually beneath surface of soil, but some species in cocoons among foliage.

14 subfamilies:

NOCTUINAE (Darts, Clays, Rustics and Others)
57 species.
Medium-sized moths. Mostly brown or greyish in colour, but some species have brightly coloured hindwings; eyes glabrous; proboscis well developed. Larvae have five pairs of prolegs; mostly night-feeders. This subfamily includes common garden species known as cutworms in their larval stage.

HADENINAE (Coronets, Quakers and Others)

65 species (1 presumed extinct in GB).

Medium-sized moths. Mostly dull brownish, greyish or ochreous in colour, but two species with brightly coloured hindwings; eyes hairy. Mostly night-flyers, but a few species fly in sunshine. Larvae have five pairs of prolegs.

CUCULLIINAE (Sharks and Others)

60 species (1 presumed extinct in GB).

Mostly medium-sized moths, but a few larger species. Proboscis usually well developed; eyes glabrous with long lashes. Most species fly at night. Some day-feeding larvae are brightly coloured; larvae have five pairs of prolegs.

ACRONICTINAE (Daggers and Others)

17 species (1 presumed extinct in GB).

Medium-sized moths. Eyes glabrous; proboscis well developed. Night-flyers. The larvae of most species are brightly coloured when well grown, and some are very hairy; all larvae have five pairs of prolegs.

AMPHIPYRINAE (Copper Underwings, Minors and Others)

96 species (3 presumed extinct in GB).

Size of the moths ranges from small to large. Eyes glabrous; proboscis well developed in most species. Most are night-flyers. Larvae have five pairs of prolegs.

HELIOTHINAE (Straws, Clovers and Others)

7 species (1 presumed extinct in GB).

Medium-sized moths. Dark marginal band on upper side of hindwings; eyes glabrous; proboscis developed. Fly fast in sunshine and at night. Larvae have five pairs of prolegs; feed on flowers and developing seeds.

ACONTIINAE (Silver Hook and Others)

8 species (1 presumed extinct in GB).

Small moths. Eyes glabrous; proboscis developed. Most species fly at night. Larvae of some species have one or two pairs of prolegs reduced and non-functional.

CHLOEPHORINAE (Green Silver-lines and Others)

5 species.

Small to medium-sized moths. Eyes glabrous; proboscis developed; forewings usually green. Night-flyers. Larvae taper towards hind segments; have five pairs of prolegs. Pupae have short dorsal spines on abdominal segments; are enclosed in papery cocoon shaped like an upturned boat.

SARROTHRIPINAE (Nycteolines)

2 species.

Small moths. Eyes glabrous; proboscis developed; costa straight; groups of raised scales present in subcostal region. Larvae have five pairs of prolegs and a few long hairs.

PANTHEINAE (Nut-tree Tussock)

1 species.

Medium-sized moth. Eyes hairy. Larvae have five pairs of prolegs; body has dorsal and lateral tufts of hairs.

PLUSIINAE (Silver Y and Others)

20 species (1 presumed extinct in GB).

Medium-sized moths. Eyes glabrous with lashes; proboscis developed; thorax and abdomen often crested; forewings may have metallic gold or silver markings. All fly at night, some also in sunshine. Larvae have reduced numbers of prolegs – in most species only three pairs are present, making the larvae semi-loopers. In pupae, haustellum free posteriorly.

CATOCALINAE (Red Underwings and Others)

10 species.

Medium-sized to large moths. Eyes glabrous; proboscis developed; when at rest, wings of many species form triangular shape. Two species fly in sunshine, otherwise night-flyers. Larvae usually have reduced numbers of prolegs; body is long and slender. Pupae covered with bluish-grey bloom.

OPHIDERINAE (Blacknecks and Others)

11 species.

Small to medium-sized moths. Eyes usually glabrous; proboscis developed in most species. Some species fly in sunshine. Larvae of most have reduced numbers of prolegs.

HYPENINAE (Snouts and Fanfoots)
16 species.
Very small to medium-sized moths. Wings form a triangle when at rest; labial palpi long, either projecting forwards (Snouts), or curved upwards; in some species males have eversible scent-brushes on their legs (e.g. Fanfoot). Night-flyers. Larvae of most species have reduced numbers of prolegs; many feed on withered leaves.

HEPIALIDAE **Common Swift**

♂ wingspan 25–30 mm

♀ wingspan 30–40 mm

IMAGO
EGG
LARVA
PUPA

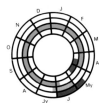

Distribution
Throughout the British Isles, but local in Scotland.

Habitat
Meadows, gardens, agricultural and horticultural land.

Life cycle
One generation a year. Over-winters as a larva.

Larval foodplants
The roots of grasses, especially couches (*Elymus* spp.), and the roots of many other wild and culti-vated plants.

Imago
The ground colour of the forewings is brown, with two irregular whitish streaks edged with dark brown. The hindwings are dark brown. The antennae are very short and simple. Females are larger, have longer wings than the males, and the markings are less well defined.

Variation is frequent, both in the extent of the white markings and in the ground colour, which sometimes can be almost white.

The moth flies from dusk onwards, and is frequently attracted to light.

Egg
The eggs are smooth and shiny, and are white when first laid, but within twenty-four hours they become jet black. They are dropped by the female while she hovers above the vegetation. Each female is capable of laying four to five hundred eggs and these hatch in about three weeks.

Larva
Directly after emergence, the larva measures 1·5 mm in length. Its general appearance does not change significantly during its lifetime. When fully grown it is shining white, with brown head and prothoracic plate, and scattered pale brown spots, each bearing a short black hair. The spir-acles are black.

The larva eats through one end of the egg to emerge, but the remainder of the shell is not eaten. It burrows down beside a root, on which it then

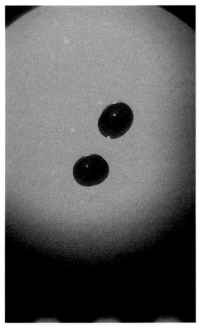

Fully-grown larva; length 35 mm

Eggs; length 0·75 mm   Pupa; length 20 mm

begins to feed. It overwinters in the ground and feeds except in the coldest weather, becoming fully grown around April. It can be a pest in agricultural ground and nursery gardens, and in private gardens, where it frequently damages crops such as turnips, parsnips, asparagus, and various herbaceous plants.

Pupa

Formed in a tunnel of silk among the roots of the larval foodplant, the pupa is roughly cylindrical with very short antennae- and wing-cases. It is pale reddish-brown and shiny, with black spiracles. The cremaster is absent. The abdominal segments have dark brown toothed dorsal ridges and bristly ventral projections, which are used to work the pupa upwards towards the surface prior to the emergence of the adult. The wingcases now darken, and the adult emerges two and a half to three weeks after pupation.

Breeding

Before attempting to rear this species in captivity, it is wise to have growing foodplant firmly established. The easiest is dandelion (*Taraxacum officinale*), upon the roots of which the larvae will thrive.

COSSIDAE (ZEUZERINAE) **Leopard Moth**

Wingspan ♂ 45–55 mm, ♀ 60–78 mm

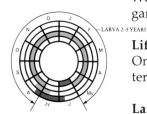

IMAGO
EGG
LARVA
PUPA

LARVA 2–3 YEARS

Distribution
England northwards to Yorkshire, and eastern Wales.

Habitat
Woodland, parkland, orchards and gardens.

Life cycle
One generation a year. Overwinters two to three years as a larva.

Larval foodplants
A wide variety of trees and shrubs, including ash (*Fraxinus excelsior*), sallow (*Salix* spp.), lilac (*Syringa vulgaris*), sycamore (*Acer pseudoplatanus*), elm (*Ulmus* spp.), and fruit trees.

Imago
The wings are white, semi-transparent, and covered with a pattern of blue-black spots. The costal and basal areas of the forewings are tinged with yellowish-brown. The thorax is white with three pairs of black spots, and the abdomen is dark grey. While the sexes are similarly marked, there are noticeable differences between them. Males are smaller than females. The antennae of the male are bipectinate in the basal half, and simple to the tip; those of the female are simple throughout the entire length. The tip of the male's abdomen bears a tuft of white hairs; the female's has a conspicuous ovipositor.

Variation sometimes occurs in the depth of colour of the blue-black spots on the wings, and occasionally some spots may be confluent.

The moth flies at night, becoming active at dusk, and is attracted to light. During the day it may

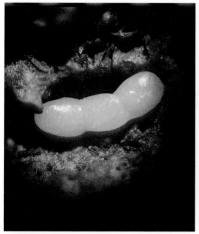

Eggs; length 1·5 mm

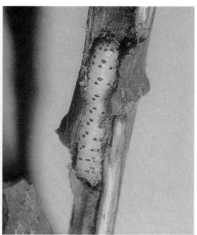

Fully-grown larva; length 55 mm

Pupa (hatched); length 42 mm

sometimes be found resting on tree trunks or fence posts, and it is often picked off by birds. The English name is derived from the leopard-like spots.

Egg

The egg is oval, tapering slightly towards one end. The surface is shiny and faintly ribbed. The colour is pale yellow, but after two weeks the larval head becomes visible through the shell, showing as a black spot. The eggs are laid sometimes singly, but more often in short rows, one overlapping the next, either on the bark or in a bark crevice. They hatch in seventeen to eighteen days.

Larva

When newly hatched, the larva is 3 mm long. The head is black and the body brownish-ochreous. When fully grown, the head, and the prothoracic and anal plates are blackish-brown. The body is yellowish-white with blackish spots, each of which bears a short hair.

The eggshell is not eaten. The freshly emerged larva immediately bores through the bark of the small branch or sapling and begins feeding under the bark. Later it penetrates through to the centre and chews upwards to form a tunnel about 15 cm long. Frass is pushed out of the original entrance hole. The larva feeds for two or three years, eventually becoming fully grown towards the end of May. When ready to pupate, the larva prepares an exit just above the original entrance hole, but leaves it covered by a thin capping of bark. Pupation takes place at the upper end of the larval tunnel.

Pupa

The pupa is reddish-brown in colour with a slightly roughened surface. On the head is a projecting beak, and the abdomen bears rows of short spines. Immediately prior to emergence the pupa works its way to the exit prepared by the larva, using the abdominal spines, ruptures the bark cap with its 'beak', and protrudes from the exit hole. The duration of the pupal stage is five to six weeks.

Breeding

In captivity, larvae have been reared on uncooked potato.

COSSIDAE (COSSINAE) **Goat Moth**

♀ wingspan 95 mm

IMAGO
EGG
LARVA
LARVA IN COCOON
PUPA

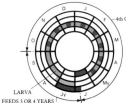

Distribution
England, Wales, central Scotland, and southern Ireland. Very scarce from the Midlands northwards.

Habitat
Mature woodland, and trees on roadside verges and river banks.

Life cycle
One generation a year. Over-winters four or five times as a larva, the last time inside a cocoon.

Larval foodplants
The living wood of a variety of deciduous trees, particularly oak (*Quercus* spp.), willow (*Salix* spp.), elm (*Ulmus* spp.), birch (*Betula* spp.), poplar (*Populus* spp.), and various fruit trees.

Imago
The forewings are greyish-brown, shaded with white and marked with wavy transverse blackish-brown lines and two black lines towards the apical area. The hindwings are greyish-brown, paler towards the margins. The thorax is greyish-brown with an ochreous collar and a black transverse line on the metathorax. The abdomen is banded alternately with dark and light grey. The sexes are similarly marked, but the female is usually considerably larger than the male, and her antennae are more shortly pectinate.

Variation can occur in the amount of white shading on the forewings.

The moth flies at night, and is occasionally attracted to light or to sugar, although it does not feed. During the day, moths may sometimes be found resting on tree-trunks, particularly just after emergence.

Egg
The eggs are roundish-oval and pale brown, striated both longitudinally and transversely with darker brown – they resemble tiny nutmegs. They are laid singly, in pairs or in small batches, either in a bark crevice or tucked under a piece of loose bark. Females tend to lay on a tree already tenanted by larvae, which is exuding sap.

Eggs; length 1·75 mm

Fully-grown larva; length 80 mm

Infested tree

Pupa; length ♂ 39 mm ♀ 45 mm

Discarded pupa case

Larva

The appearance of the larva changes very little throughout its long life. When fully grown, the head and prothoracic plate are black; the body, which is nipped in tightly between each segment, is brownish-red dorsally and pinkish-ochreous ventrally. There are sparse short pale hairs, and the large spiracles are brown.

In its early stages the larva lives just beneath the bark, making grooves in the wood as it eats, but as it matures it bores more deeply into the trunk. One tree will be host to successive generations of larvae, and may be recognised by the holes in the bark, the loss of pieces of bark, the exposed grooves in the wood, and by woodpecker damage. During the summer sawdust falls from the holes and sap runs freely. As the running sap ferments, it gives off a characteristic 'beery' smell, which is noticeable several yards from the tree. The moth's English name derives from the supposedly goat-like smell of the larva, but this is not always detectable. During the autumn of its final year, the larva often emerges from the host tree and ranges widely in search of a pupation site. It remains dormant in a cocoon throughout the winter, pupating towards the end of May or beginning of June the following spring.

Pupa

The pupa is shiny with a finely roughened surface. It is light reddish-brown with paler abdominal segments. The last segment, and the head with its prominent projecting beak, are dark reddish-brown. The abdominal segments bear transverse rows of short dark reddish-brown spines. Female pupae are much larger than males. The pupa is contained in a very tough cocoon of yellowish silk reinforced with chips of wood or particles of soil. This may be either inside the host tree, or just below the surface of the soil up against a buttress root or similar solid object. Immediately prior to emergence of the moth, the pupa breaks through the cocoon and works itself out into the open with the aid of its abdominal spines. The extruded pupa cases may sometimes be found. The pupal stage lasts four to five weeks.

Breeding

Keeping Goat Moth larvae in captivity poses certain problems. With its strong jaws the larva can – and will – eat its way out of a wooden or net cage, and must therefore be kept in a metal or glass container with some larva-proof means of ventilation. It will feed on a continual supply of freshly cut logs, but feeding is simplified if the larva can be persuaded to eat uncooked beetroot, as this will speed up its development considerably – larvae have been reared to maturity in one year on this diet. Large old beetroot are most suitable. The larva will construct its cocoon in fresh sawdust.

ZYGAENIDAE (PROCRIDINAE) **Cistus Forester**

Wingspan ♂ 19–25 mm, ♀ 18–21 mm

IMAGO
EGG
LARVA
PUPA

Distribution
Calcareous areas of southern England, North Wales, and the Midlands up to Cumbria and Durham.

Habitat
Chalk downland and limestone hills.

Life cycle
One generation a year. Over-winters as a larva.

Larval foodplant
Common rock-rose (*Helianthemum nummularium*).

Imago
The forewings, head, antennae, body and legs are metallic green or yellowish-green, and the hind-wings grey-brown. The antennae of the male are bipectinate at the base and thickened at the tip; those of the female are slightly dentate and more slender. Females are smaller than males.

Variation occurs in the ground colour of the forewings, from green to yellow-green.

This is a day-flying moth, and in sunshine it actively visits flowers such as trefoils, rock-roses and knapweeds. Late in the afternoon it may often be found at rest on grass stems or flower heads such as knapweed and scabious.

Egg
The eggs are pale yellow, slightly ribbed and reticulated. They are laid either singly or in small groups on the underside of leaves of the food-plant. Usually a well established rock-rose, on an old anthill, is selected. The eggs hatch in about ten to twelve days.

Larva
When newly hatched, the head of the larva is black and the body yellowish-ochreous with short hairs. After the first moult and until the larva is fully grown, the body is stumpy, with longitudinal markings of purplish-brown and cream. Short bristles are attached to purplish tubercles. The

Eggs; length 1 mm

1st instar larvae; length 1·25 mm

Fully-grown larva; length 13 mm

Cocoon; length 13 mm

Pupa; length 9 mm

small retractile head is black, and the prothoracic plate dark brown, edged along the front with yellow.

The eggshell is not eaten on emergence. The young larva burrows under the lower cuticle of the leaf, forming a blotch-like mine. After a few weeks the lower cuticle is consumed. Hibernation takes place in the litter beneath the foodplant, and feeding recommences in spring, when the whole substance of the leaf is eaten. When not feeding, the larva rests deep down among stems at the base of the foodplant. If disturbed, the larva rolls up into a ring. It feeds during the day, but avoids bright sunlight.

Pupa

The cocoon is fusiform, and is made of loosely spun greyish-white, whitish or yellowish silk. It is spun deep down among the stems of the rock-rose. The pupa is olive green, with the abdomen the palest part of the body. The wingcases are shiny with a slightly roughened surface. The tongue case is long, and free towards the tip. The abdominal segments have transverse dorsal rows of small bristles. The larval skin is not retained. The adult emerges in three to four weeks, and shortly before this the pupa becomes greenish-mahogany and works forwards to the anterior end of the cocoon.

Breeding

Although larvae may be fed successfully on cut foodplant after hibernation, growing rock-rose is essential during the early instars, when the larvae burrow inside leaves. If cut food is used at this time, the wilting of the leaves will result in the loss of the larvae within.

ZYGAENIDAE (ZYGAENINAE) **Six-spot Burnet**

Wingspan 25–40 mm

IMAGO
EGG
LARVA
PUPA

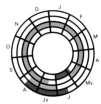

Distribution
Throughout England, Wales, and Ireland. In Scotland confined to coastal districts.

Habitat
Meadows, roadside verges, chalk downs, sand hills, cliffs, and woodland rides.

Life cycle
One generation a year. Over-winters as a larva, sometimes twice.

Larval foodplants
Bird's-foot trefoil (*Lotus corniculatus*), clovers (*Trifolium* spp.).

Imago
Each forewing has six red spots, prominent against the ground colour, which is black with a metallic greenish sheen. The hindwings are red with a narrow black border. The head and body share the ground colour of the forewings, and the legs are black. The antennae end in a pointed club. The sexes are similar.

Variation occurs frequently in the size and shade of the red spots, and in their shape – two or more may be confluent. Sometimes specimens occur in which all the red colour is replaced by yellow (f. *flava*).

The moth flies by day, and is most active in sunshine, when it visits flowers such as knapweeds, thistles, scabious, hawkweeds and orchids. In dull weather and during the evening it rests on flower heads and grass stems. Pairing takes place immediately after the female emerges from the pupa.

Egg
The eggs are yellow, slightly reticulated, and transparent at one end. They are laid in several layers in batches on the undersides of leaves – not necessarily on the foodplant – and hatch in eight to ten days. One day before hatching the colour becomes dark grey.

Egg batch

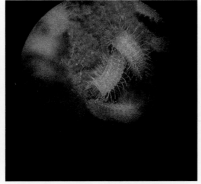

1st instar larvae; length 1·5 mm

Fully-grown larva; length 18 mm

Cocoon; length 30 mm

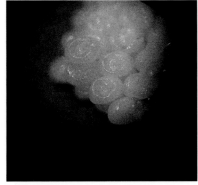

Eggs; length 1 mm

Larva in May; length 7 mm

Pupa; length 20 mm

Larva

Immediately after hatching, the head of the larva is black, and the body yellowish-ochre with white hairs. After moulting and until hibernation the ground colour is green. During hibernation it becomes brown, reverting to green in the spring. The fully grown larva is greenish-yellow with black and yellow spots and a black head.

The eggshell is not eaten. The larva feeds during the day on the foodplant leaves. It goes into hibernation at the base of the plant during the fourth instar, and becomes active again towards the end of April. Some then feed up and pupate, but others only feed for a few weeks and then go into hibernation again when 7 to 8 mm long. These latter are not fully grown until the following year. If disturbed, the larva drops from the foodplant and rolls into a ring.

Pupa

The cocoon is fusiform, longitudinally ribbed, of a papery texture, glossy, and either yellow or white in colour. It is attached to a grass stem or other such support and is usually quite exposed.

The pupa is black, with the wingcases and thorax glossy and the abdomen duller. The edges of the wingcases and end of the tongue case are free from the rest of the pupa. The abdominal segments bear ridges of sharp, backward-facing raised points. If the cocoon is disturbed, the pupa audibly scrapes these against the walls of the cocoon. The moth emerges two to three weeks after pupation. Before this, the pupa breaks through the anterior end of the cocoon and half-emerges. When the moth has flown, the empty pupa case is left protruding from the cocoon.

Breeding

Larvae may be reared entirely on cut foodplant, but this may be a lengthy process due to the tendency for some to overwinter twice.

LIMACODIDAE **The Festoon**

♂ wingspan 26 mm

♀ wingspan 30–32 mm

IMAGO
EGG
LARVA
LARVA IN COCOON
PUPA

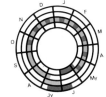

Distribution
Southern England as far north as Northamptonshire and Worcestershire.

Habitat
Oak woodland, and smaller oaks bordering heathland.

Life cycle
One generation a year. Overwinters as a fully grown larva inside its cocoon.

Larval foodplants
Oak (*Quercus* spp.), and beech (*Fagus sylvatica*).

Imago
The forewings of the male are ochreous brown transversed by two dark brown lines and shaded with darker brown. The hindwings are purplish-brown and the antennae slightly pectinate. The female is slightly larger, and both fore- and hind-wings are pale ochreous brown, the forewings bearing two dark brown transverse lines similar to those of the male. Her antennae are simple.

Variation is more often found in the male – the amount of black suffusion on the forewings varies, and the ground colour of the wings may resemble that of the female.

The moth flies mainly at night, although it is occasionally reported as flying high round oaks in sunshine. Females may sometimes be beaten from the lower branches of oaks during the day. Both sexes come to light.

Egg
The egg is large for the size of the moth. It is oval, flattened, and bears faint reticulations, visible under magnification. Scales from the female's abdomen are frequently attached to it. The egg is laid singly on the underside of a leaf; at first it appears almost transparent, but becomes yellowish after two days. The colour then gradually becomes greyer, and the egg hatches after ten to twelve days.

Larva
When newly hatched, the head is black and the body white and spiny. After successive moults the body becomes greener and the spines shorter. When fully grown the body is bright green with two wavy subdorsal ridges, each marked with

Apoda limacodes (HUFNAGEL)

 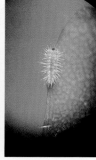 

Egg; length 1·5 mm
1st instar larva; length 1 mm

Larva before final moult; length 11 mm

Fully-grown larva; length 15 mm

Larva; ventral surface

Cocoon among fallen leaves

Hatched cocoon; length 9 mm
Pupa; length 7 mm

pink spots. Behind the retractile head is a yellow line round the front edge of the first abdominal segment. The ventral surface of the body is whitish and the prolegs are absent, being replaced by minute suckers. Just before the larva spins its cocoon, its colour becomes greenish-yellow and the pink spots disappear.

The eggshell is not eaten. The larva rests on the underside of a leaf and feeds at the edge. Until it is about 5 mm long, the larva feeds only on the lower cuticle, leaving the upper cuticle intact. This produces a brown filigree pattern on the leaf. After this, it eats the whole substance of the leaf at the tip, feeding actively in sunshine. Due to the absence of prolegs, locomotion consists of a gliding motion with a slight side-to-side rocking. The ventral suckers adhere very firmly to a ribbon of silk which is laid down by the larva, and which in appearance resembles a slug trail. A sideways view of a moving larva reveals a succession of wave-like motions travelling forwards from the tail end along the ventral surface. Towards the end

of September or the beginning of October, the larva spins a tough, oval, reddish-brown cocoon, which may be found attached to a dead leaf in the litter beneath the tree, usually 30 to 40 cm away from the trunk, and 2 to 5 cm deep. The larva hibernates within this cocoon until the following May, when it pupates.

Pupa

The pupa is whitish in colour. The thorax and wingcases are shiny and the eyes dark. Between the eyes is a small beak-like appendage for rupturing the cocoon. The legs and wingcases are free from the rest of the pupa case. The abdomen, which is dull in appearance, has transverse yellowish bands and a number of tiny backward-pointing spines. The larval skin is attached to the cremaster. When ready to hatch, the pupa works itself forward within the cocoon. It breaks open the front section, which swings aside like a lid to allow the pupa to push out. The pupal stage lasts for two and a half to three weeks.

SESIIDAE (SESIINAE) **Lunar Hornet Moth**

♀ wingspan 42 mm

IMAGO
EGG
LARVA
PUPA

LARVA 2 YEARS

Distribution
Throughout the British Isles.

Habitat
Open damp woodland, marshy areas with well-grown *Salix*, and wet heathland.

Life cycle
One generation a year. Over-winters twice as a larva.

Larval foodplants
The wood of well-grown sallows and willows (*Salix* spp.). Also recorded from poplar (*Populus* spp.).

Imago
Sexually dimorphic. The head is black, the thorax black with a yellow collar, and the abdomen banded in black and yellow. The legs are yellow and reddish-yellow. The wings are mainly transparent and the antennae black, thickened below the apex but tapering to the tips, which are curved. The male has lamellate antennae, and the wings are edged and veined with blackish-brown. The female is usually slightly larger than the male, her antennae are smooth, and the wing edges and veins are reddish-brown. The very similar species, the Hornet Moth (*S. apiformis*), differs in being rather larger than the Lunar Hornet, and having a yellow head and a broken yellow collar, and mainly reddish-brown legs.

Variation can occur in the amount of black or brownish shading on the abdominal segments.

The moths fly by day, and are active in sunshine. Soon after emergence and in dull weather

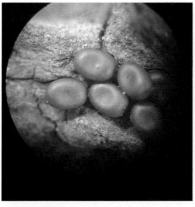

Eggs; length 1 mm   Fully-grown larva; length 30 mm   Pupa; length 29 mm

they may be found resting on sallow or willow trunks. The English name derives from the moth's extraordinary resemblance to the hornet (*Vespa crabro*).

Egg
The eggs are oval, flattened, and reddish-brown in colour, with a slightly grainy surface. They are laid in small batches, usually of eight to fifteen eggs, on the trunk of the foodplant, 0·75 to 2 m above ground level, and hatch in three to four weeks.

Larva
When newly hatched, the larva is 2·5 mm long, the head and prothoracic plate are brown, and the body is ochreous with a pinkish tinge which deepens towards the anal claspers. The body bears short, sparse, pale hairs. When the larva is fully grown, the head is dark reddish-brown with black-tipped mandibles, the prothoracic plate is yellowish-brown with two fine brown diagonal lines, and the body, which has short, sparse dark bristles, is yellowish-white, plump, and very wrinkled.

The eggshell is not eaten. The larva emerges from one end of the shell and immediately begins to tunnel beneath the bark near the base of the trunk, extruding reddish frass from the tunnel entrance. During the second year, the larva burrows more deeply into the trunk, boring vertically about 1·5 cm beneath the inner surface of the bark. When fully grown during the autumn, the larva constructs an exit by gnawing a tunnel leading back towards the bark. This outer layer is left intact, and the tunnel is thus safely sealed and the boring very difficult to detect. The best indication of the presence of either larvae or pupae are gashes in a tree trunk made by woodpeckers seeking a meal.

Pupa
The pupa is smooth, shiny, and yellowish-brown, with darker colouring between the segments. On the dorsal surface of the abdominal segments are rows of short, dark brown, backward-pointing spines; the cremaster bears more spines, and there is a beak-like projection between the eyes. The pupa, which wriggles a great deal, is contained head-down in a very tough cocoon of silk mixed with chewed wood, situated in the upper part of a boring 5 to 10 cm above the exit hole. Just before emergence the pupa becomes blackish. It ruptures the cocoon, works its way to the exit, breaks through the tunnel cap, and protrudes from the tree-trunk. It hatches five to six weeks after pupation.

Breeding
Breeding this species from egg to adult is extremely difficult, due to the near-impossibility of providing the correct conditions over a long period. Larvae may be reared from the egg over the first winter in cut sections of sallow or willow which have been dipped in rooting powder and are standing in damp sand, but after this the wood tends to dry out and the larvae are lost.

SESIIDAE (PARANTHRENINAE) **Large Red-belted Clearwing**

Wingspan 22–28 mm

IMAGO
EGG
LARVA
PUPA

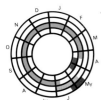

Distribution
England and Wales. Less wide-spread in Scotland.

Habitat
Open woodland and heathland.

Life cycle
One generation a year. Over-winters as a fully grown larva.

Larval foodplant
The stumps of recently felled birch (*Betula* spp.).

Imago
The wings are hyaline with blue-black veins. In the forewing, the costa and dorsum are black, and there is a red patch at the base. The head, antennae, legs and body are blue-black, the abdomen having a red belt round the fourth segment. The anal tuft is black.

There is an uncommon variation – ab. *flavocingulata* – in which the red belt and forewing patches are replaced by yellow.

This is a day-flying species, and the moths are active in sunshine. In dull weather they may be found resting on vegetation. In flight they resemble a parasitic wasp. The females may be seen ovipositing during the afternoons, inserting eggs in crevices of birch stumps felled one or two years previously.

Egg
The eggs, which are laid singly deep inside crevices in birch bark, are dark reddish-brown in colour, covered with fine white reticulations.

Larva
The appearance of the larva changes little throughout its life. When fully grown, the body is white with short brown hairs. The head is reddish-brown, and on the prothorax are two reddish-brown diagonal marks.

The larva lives and feeds under the bark of birch stumps, usually in the upper portion. It eats out a

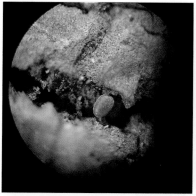

Egg; length 0·7 mm

Fully-grown larva; length 15 mm

Cocoon; length 25 mm

Pupa; length 14 mm

Extruded pupa case

Affected birch stump

tunnel between the bark and the wood, and then feeds in this. Frass is pushed out of the tunnel, the larva using its head as a shovel. The exit hole is usually situated on the top of the stump, and during late summer the little heaps of reddish-brown frass round the edges of the stump give a good indication of the presence of larvae within. By early spring most of the frass has generally been blown away, but the holes – each 2 to 3 mm in diameter – are clearly visible. During the winter or early spring the larva uses particles of wood and silk to construct a fibrous cocoon within the larval tunnel, approximately 30 to 60 mm below the exit hole.

Pupa
The pupa is pale, shiny and yellowish-brown, with transverse bands of dark brown backward-facing spines on the dorsal surface of the abdominal segments. Just before emergence of the adult moth, the whole pupa becomes black in colour. It works its way upwards using the abdominal spines, ruptures the cocoon, and protrudes from the exit hole. Newly emerged moths may be found resting on the birch stumps; the empty pupa cases often remain in position for some time, and are very conspicuous.

Breeding
Although this species has a one-year life cycle, it is still very difficult to maintain the correct conditions for breeding from egg to adult. Success may be achieved if stumps containing larvae are collected during late summer, bedded in damp sand and placed outdoors in partial shade.

LASIOCAMPIDAE **The Lackey**

♂ wingspan 30–35 mm

IMAGO
EGG
LARVA
PUPA

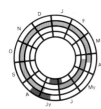

Distribution
England (scarcer in the north), Wales, and Ireland.

Habitat
Woodlands, hedgerows, bushy places, and gardens.

Life cycle
One generation a year. Overwinters as an egg.

Larval foodplants
A wide variety of trees and shrubs, including blackthorn (*Prunus spinosa*), hawthorn (*Crataegus monogyna*), sallow (*Salix* spp.), hazel (*Corylus avellana*), birch (*Betula* spp.), oak (*Quercus* spp.), and various fruit trees.

Imago
The wings are reddish-brown or yellowish, with two pale cross-lines on the forewings. The head and body are of similar colour to the wings. The antennae of the male are pectinate. The female is larger than the male, her antennae are ciliate, and the area between the cross-lines on her forewings is usually darker than the rest of the ground colour.

Variation occurs very frequently – the ground colour of the wings ranges from pale yellow to deep red-brown.

The moth flies at night, and is attracted to light.

Egg
The eggs are purplish-brown in colour. The sunken micropyle is deep purple, and is surrounded by a grey ring edged with deep purple. The eggs are laid in a batch forming a bracelet round a twig of the foodplant, and the spaces between the eggs are filled with a hard clear substance which gives a very varnished appearance to the batch. Laid the previous year, the eggs hatch towards the end of April.

Larva
When newly hatched, the larva is 2 mm long; its

  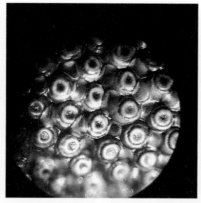 

♀ laying eggs
Egg batch on apple twig

Eggs; width 1 mm

Larval web

Larvae in May; length 14 mm

Fully-grown larva; length 50 mm

Pupa; length 19 mm

head is black, and its body black with long white hairs. As it grows, the body colouring becomes more striking – black with orange, white, and blue stripes. When the larva is fully grown, the head is blue with two black spots looking like eye-spots, and the body is blue with a white dorsal line. Below this line are a series of black, red and orange stripes. The body bears long reddish hairs.

The eggshell is not eaten. When young, the larvae live gregariously in a dense web of whitish silk spun on a twig of the foodplant. Both occupied and deserted webs are very conspicuous. In the final instar the larvae leave the web and become solitary. Large numbers of them can be destructive to fruit trees in gardens and orchards.

Pupa
The pupa is dull and black, with short reddish hairs on the thorax and abdomen. It is enclosed in a double cocoon spun among leaves and twigs of the foodplant. The outer, thin cocoon is of whitish silk. The denser inner one is impregnated with a fine sulphur-coloured powder – as it pupated, the larva produced a liquid which dried to form this substance. The adult moth emerges in about two weeks.

LASIOCAMPIDAE **Oak Eggar**

♂ wingspan 65 mm

♀ wingspan 88 mm

IMAGO ▪
EGG ▪
LARVA ▪
PUPA ▪

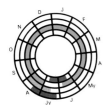

Distribution
England, as far north as Lancashire and Durham.

Habitat
Woodland, downland, commons, and sea-cliffs.

Life cycle
One generation a year. Over-winters as a young larva.

Larval foodplants
A wide variety of trees and shrubs, including hawthorn (*Crataegus monogyna*), bramble (*Rubus fruticosus*), sallow (*Salix* spp.), blackthorn (*Prunus spinosa*), gorse (*Ulex* spp.), broom (*Cytisus scoparius*).

Imago
The wings of the male are dark reddish-brown, crossed by a band of orange-yellow, sharply defined on the inner edge but shaded towards the outer margins of the wings. The forewing has a prominent white discal spot and the antennae are strongly pectinate. The female is larger than the male, the wings much paler, the white discal spot ringed with dark reddish-brown, and the antennae shortly serrate.

Variation can occur in the depth of the ground colour and extent of the bands.

Females fly only at night, but males are active during the day and may be seen in sunshine flying very vigorously in search of resting females.

Egg
The eggs are oval, smooth and shining. They are ochreous in colour, marked with a pattern of dark brown mottling. They are dropped by the female while in flight, and fall freely into the herbage. They hatch after about two and a half weeks.

Larva
When newly hatched, the larva has a black head, and a black body with long white hairs and orange between the segments. Before hibernation the body is greyish-black with orange bands and a

Egg; length 2 mm

1st instar larva; length 7 mm

Larva before hibernation; length 20 mm

Fully-grown larva; length 54 mm

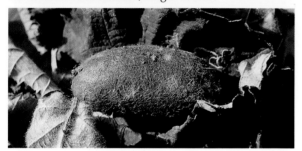

Cocoon; length 30 mm

Pupa; length 28 mm

dorsal row of creamy-white marks. After hibernation the colouring is more subdued, and when fully grown the body is brownish-grey and thickly covered with ochreous-brown hairs. There is a broken white lateral stripe with reddish marks beneath it.

The eggshell is not eaten. The larva is sluggish in its movements, and if disturbed falls to the ground and rolls into a ring. It feeds at night, and during the day either leaves the foodplant altogether or rests very low down on the stems. It begins hibernation during October, and recommences feeding about April.

Pupa
The pupa is fairly smooth except for the tail end which bears short reddish bristles. Its abdomen is dark reddish-brown, and its thorax and wingcases purplish-brown. It is enclosed in a very hard oval cocoon, the egg-like shape of which gives the species the name Eggar. The outside of the cocoon is dark grey with short reddish hairs adhering, and the inside white, also with reddish hairs. The usual situation for the cocoon is in litter on the surface of the ground, although sometimes it may be spun among twigs of the foodplant.

LASIOCAMPIDAE **Fox Moth**

♂ wingspan 55 mm

♀ wingspan 70 mm

IMAGO
EGG
LARVA
PUPA

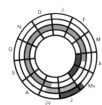

Distribution
Throughout the British Isles.

Habitat
Downland, heathland, woodland and waste ground.

Life cycle
One generation a year. Over-winters as a fully grown larva.

Larval foodplants
A wide variety of plants including bramble (*Rubus fruticosus*), bilberry (*Vaccinium myrtillus*), heather (*Calluna vulgaris*), heaths (*Erica* spp.), and the flowers of dwarf gorse (*Ulex minor*).

Imago
The body and wings of the male are reddish-brown, and the antennae are pectinate. The body and wings of the female, which is slightly larger, are greyish-brown, and her antennae are serrate.

Both sexes have two ochreous transverse lines across the forewings.

Variation can occur in the ground colour, particularly that of the male, which can range from dark red-brown to greyish-brown. Females from southern England are usually lighter in colour than those from other parts of the British Isles.

The Fox Moth gets its English name from the fox-colour of the male's wings. The male is active by day, and may be seen in sunshine flying swiftly and erratically in search of a female. The females rest in herbage during the day, and only fly at night, when they are attracted to light.

Egg
The eggs are oval, slightly flattened, ochreous in colour, and patterned with a clouding of pale brown. The shells are smooth and shiny. They are laid in batches around the stems of the foodplants, and hatch in two and a half to three weeks.

Larva
When newly hatched, the larva is 6 mm long; the head and body are black with pale yellow between

Egg batch on heather

Eggs; length 2 mm

Larva before final moult; length 50 mm

Fully-grown larva; length 60 mm

Cocoon; length 45 mm

Pupa; length 31 mm

the segments. The body is covered with long black hairs with some white ones mixed in. During the middle instars, the body is brownish-black with yellow between the segments on the dorsal surface, and is covered with reddish-brown hairs. Low down on the sides are tufts of white hairs. When fully grown, the head and body are black and covered with thick reddish hairs, with white hairs along the sides.

The eggshell is eaten. The larva feeds at night, and during the day rests among herbage near the foodplant. If disturbed it rolls into a ring. It feeds until fully grown, in September or October, and then hibernates, emerging in March to sun itself. Some larvae feed sparingly after hibernation; others do not feed at all. Care should be exercised when handling this larva, as the hairs can be irritant and cause unpleasant skin reactions in some people.

Pupa

The pupa is blackish-brown, with a more reddish colour between the abdominal segments. Its wing-cases and the first few segments of its abdomen are slightly roughened. It is enclosed in a long slender cocoon of dark grey silk mixed with larval hairs which is woven in a more or less upright position in moss, leaf litter, or low herbage. The adult moth emerges in four to five weeks.

Breeding

Fox Moth larvae are notoriously difficult to over-winter successfully. However, I have found the following method to be very satisfactory:

Take a large plastic seed tray with drainage holes in the base. Put in a layer of sterile potting soil, and cover it with a thick layer of reindeer lichen (*Cladonia portentosa*) and a few dead leaves which have been carefully sorted over for predators. Embed some thick stems of bramble and laurel in the soil – they will remain fresh for a long time, and provide food if the larvae need it. Cover the whole tray with rot-proof nylon netting supported on curved wires, and place outdoors in a position of semi-shade with some means of keeping off the heaviest rain. Place the fully grown larvae in the tray when they appear to have ceased feeding. They should reappear to sun themselves in the early spring before pupating among the lichen.

LASIOCAMPIDAE **The Drinker**

♂ wingspan 60 mm

♀ wingspan 70 mm

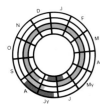

IMAGO
EGG
LARVA
PUPA

Distribution
England, Wales, Ireland, and western Scotland.

Habitat
Damp situations, including woodland rides, damp moorland, fenland, and margins of ditches and lanes.

Life cycle
One generation a year. Overwinters as a young larva.

Larval foodplants
Grasses, including cocks-foot (*Dactylis glomerata*) and couches (*Elymus* spp.), reeds such as common reed (*Phragmites australis*), sedges (*Carex* spp.), and small-reeds (*Calamagrostis* spp.).

Imago
The wings of the male are rich reddish-brown, the forewings shaded with purplish-brown and crossed by two dark brown lines. There is a prominent creamy-white discal spot with a smaller similar spot above it. The antennae are strongly pectinate. Females are larger than males; the wings are similarly marked, but the ground colour is yellowish-ochreous. The antennae are weakly pectinate. The palpi of both sexes are long, and form a prominent 'beak'.

Variation occurs in the ground colour and in the size and shape of the white spots. The lines on the wings may be less prominent or even absent.

The moth flies at night and is attracted to light.

Egg
The eggs are oval, smooth and shiny. They are bluish-white in colour with darker greenish-blue markings. They are laid in small batches on the foodplants, and hatch in about two weeks.

Larva
When newly hatched, the larva is 5 mm long and dark brown with longitudinal rows of orange tubercles bearing long brown hairs. Just before hibernation the head is still brown, but immediately behind it there is a conspicuous black

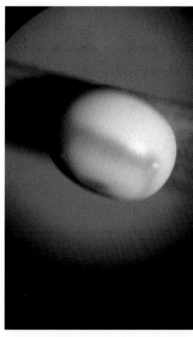

Larvae before hibernation; length 13 mm

Fully-grown larva; length 60 mm

Egg; length 2 mm

Cocoon; length 42 mm

Pupa; length 26 mm

mark; the body is patterned with black, white and yellow, and bears fine brown hairs. When the larva is fully grown, it is bluish-grey with subdorsal rows of orange spots. Along the spiracular region are more orange spots and tufts of white hairs. The body is covered with fine yellowish-brown hairs. There are two conspicuous tufts of blackish hairs, one on the second segment and the other on the eleventh.

Part of the eggshell is eaten. The larva feeds until about September and then hibernates. It recommences feeding in March. If disturbed it rolls into a ring. The name 'Drinker' was given to this species because the larva has been observed drinking drops of dew.

Pupa

The blunt-ended pupa is smooth, not shiny, and dark brown with a slight reddish-brown tinge between the last segments. It is enclosed in a slender, quite tough cocoon of whitish or yellowish-white silk attached to a stem of the foodplant. The adult moth emerges in about three weeks.

SATURNIIDAE **Emperor Moth**

♂ wingspan 68 mm

♀ wingspan 85 mm

IMAGO
EGG
LARVA
PUPA

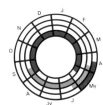

Distribution
Throughout the British Isles.

Habitat
Heathland, moorland, woodland, waste ground, mosses, and commons.

Life cycle
One generation a year. Overwinters as a pupa.

Larval foodplants
A wide range of plants including bramble (*Rubus fruticosus*), heather (*Calluna vulgaris*), heaths (*Erica* spp.), sallow (*Salix* spp.), blackthorn (*Prunus spinosa*), hawthorn (*Crataegus monogyna*), alder buckthorn (*Frangula alnus*).

Imago
The forewings of the male are variegated with shades of grey or brownish-grey, cream, and rosy red. In the centre of the wing is a white patch containing a large black, yellow and blue eye-spot. The hindwings are orange with a similar eye-spot and a broad black band towards the outer margin. The antennae are strongly pectinate. The female is larger, and the markings are similar to those of the male, but the ground colour is pale grey. Her antennae are pale yellow and serrate.

Variation can occur in the ground colour of the wings and in the size and shape of the eye-spots.

The male flies by day, and is able to detect the presence of a female from a distance of up to a kilometre. Females sit in heather or low herbage during the day, and only fly at night. As soon as the wings are expanded and hardened after emergence, the female begins 'calling' – giving off pheromones to attract a male. Pairing usually takes place within a few hours of emergence, and lasts about one hour.

Egg
The eggs are oval with a depression in the upper surface, and are faintly marked with longitudinal striations. They are brownish-ochreous with darker brown clouding, and usually have a few hairs from the female's abdomen adhering to them. They are laid in batches round the stems or twigs of the foodplant, and when laid on heather they closely resemble a cluster of dried heather flowers. They hatch in about four weeks.

Larva
When newly hatched, the larva has a shiny black head, and a black body with short black hairs. In

Egg batch on heather

Egg; length 2 mm

1st instar larvae; length 5 mm

3rd instar larva; length 17 mm

4th instar larva; length 25 mm

Fully-grown larva; length 65 mm

Cocoon; length 50 mm

Cocoons & pupa; pupa length 25 mm

the second instar there is a broken yellow spiracular line. In the third instar this line is orange, and there are orange bands on the sides of the larva. In the next instar the body is ringed with orange, with the orange spiracular line still prominent, and short hairs are present over the whole body. When fully grown, the head is green with black lines, and the body green with a thin yellow subspiracular line. On each segment is a black band with pink, white, yellow or orange warts, each wart bearing black hairs. The spiracles are orange.

The eggshell is not eaten. The larvae are gregarious until after the third moult, when they sep-arate. Although quite conspicuous in the earlier instars, the fully grown larva is surprisingly well camouflaged, especially when resting on heather.

Pupa

The pupa is dark brown, with reddish-brown on the abdominal segments. The surface is slightly roughened. It is contained in a stout, tough, flask-shaped cocoon of brown silk spun among the stems of the foodplant. The moth emerges through the narrow end of the cocoon, the fibres of which close up behind the moth, leaving no sign of its departure.

ENDROMIDAE **Kentish Glory**

♂ wingspan 55–65 mm

♀ wingspan 75–85 mm

IMAGO ■
EGG ▪
LARVA ▪
PUPA ■

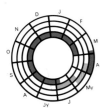

Distribution
Restricted to a few localities in the Highland region of Scotland.

Habitat
Moorland with birch, and open woodland.

Life cycle
One generation a year. Over-winters as a pupa, sometimes two or three times.

Larval foodplants
Birch (*Betula* spp.). Has been recorded on alder (*Alnus glutinosa*).

Imago
In the male the forewings are brown, marked with reddish-brown and white. There are two black cross-lines edged with white and a black V-shaped discal mark. The hindwings are orange-brown, marked with brown and white, and with a wavy black line. The antennae are strongly pectinate. The female's wings are similarly marked to those of the male, but the ground colour is light brown. She is larger, and her antennae are weakly pectinate.

Variation can occur in the shade of the ground colour.

Although formerly resident in Kent and parts of central and southern England, the Kentish Glory is now restricted to parts of Scotland, where it is very local. The males fly swiftly and strongly in sunshine, but the females do not become active until dusk.

Egg
The eggs are oblong, smooth and shiny; yellowish when laid, they become brown after a few days. They are deposited in short rows, often in two layers, on the twigs of the foodplant, and hatch in about three weeks.

Larva
When newly hatched, the larva is 5 mm long with

Eggs; length 2 mm

1st instar larva; length 7 mm

2nd instar larvae; length 12 mm

3rd instar larva; length 23 mm

Fully-grown larva; length 50 mm

Pupa; length 25 mm

a black head, a dark chocolate brown body, ochreous colouring between the segments, and an ochreous-brown collar behind the head. The body bears a few short black hairs, and has a conspicuous bump on the eleventh segment. After the first moult the larva becomes more greenish, with dark lines on the back and faint oblique stripes on the sides. When it is fully grown its body is green, thickly freckled with black spots. On either side of its head and first three segments there is a creamy line. All along its sides there are oblique creamy lines, and there is a prominent horn-like projection on the eleventh segment. The large oval spiracles are white.

The eggshell is not eaten. When young, the larvae are gregarious, and sit in groups near the tips of the twigs, with the fore-part of the body bent backwards away from the twig. In later instars the larvae are solitary, and usually rest on the underside of a twig. When the larva is about to pupate, its ground colour becomes deep rose pink.

Pupa
The pupa is blackish-brown and dull, with a rough surface. On the dorsal surface of the abdomen are transverse rows of short backward-pointing hooks with which the pupa works itself partially out of the cocoon before the emergence of the moth. The tough cocoon, composed of an open network of blackish silk covered with debris, is found in litter on the surface of the ground under the foodplant. The pupa may overwinter two or three times.

DREPANIDAE **Oak Hook-tip**

♂ wingspan 30 mm

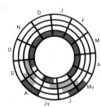

Distribution
England, as far north as Westmorland and Yorkshire, and in most parts of Wales.

Habitat
Woodland and parks with oaks.

Life cycle
Two generations a year. Overwinters as a pupa.

Larval foodplant
Oak (*Quercus* spp.).

Imago
The wings of the male are rich ochreous-brown, traversed by two yellowish lines. On each forewing are two black discal spots; on the hindwings there are similar spots, but they are much fainter. The wingtips are hooked. Females are larger, and their hindwings are yellower than those of the male. The antennae of the male are pectinate; those of the female are simple.

Variation may occur in the ground colour, and this may sometimes be shaded with purplish-brown, especially in the male.

Although mainly a night-flyer, the moth may sometimes be seen flying in sunshine, and can also be disturbed from among fallen leaves, where the shape and colour of the wings afford excellent camouflage. It is attracted to light.

Egg
The eggs are oval, longitudinally ribbed and very shiny. When first laid they are creamy-white, but they begin to go pink after twenty-four hours. They are laid singly on the underside of a leaf of the foodplant, usually close to the edge, and hatch in about seven days.

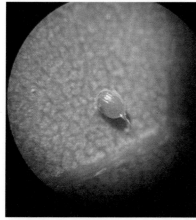

Egg; length 0·75 mm

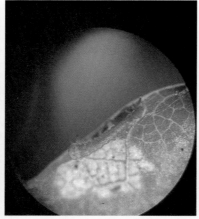

2nd instar larva; length 8 mm

Cocoon; length 15 mm

Pupa; length 10 mm

Fully-grown larva; length 15 mm

Larva

When newly hatched, the larva is 1·5 mm long, and dark brown with a pale brown head. When fully grown the body is ochreous-brown, shaded with darker brown. There is a yellowish brown 'saddle' mark edged with chocolate brown, and two conspicuous raised points on the third segment. The anal claspers are absent, and the tail end is raised.

The eggshell is not eaten. In the early instars the larva 'filigrees' the leaf, but later the whole substance of the leaf is eaten. The larvae normally rest exposed on the upper surface of foodplant leaves.

Pupa

The pupa is pale green, smooth, and not shiny. It is contained in a semi-transparent cocoon of yellowish-white silk spun on the underside of a leaf of the foodplant. In those individuals that do not overwinter, the adult emerges in seven to ten days.

THYATIRIDAE **Buff Arches**

Wingspan 40–44 mm

IMAGO
EGG
LARVA
PUPA

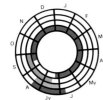

Distribution
Throughout Wales, England as far north as Yorkshire, and most parts of Ireland.

Habitat
Woodland, waste ground, commons, and other bushy places.

Life cycle
One generation a year. Overwinters as a pupa.

Larval foodplant
Bramble (*Rubus fruticosus*). Has been recorded on raspberry (*R. idaeus*).

Imago
The forewings are pale grey marked with reddish-brown and crossed by wavy lines and straighter streaks of reddish-brown and cream. The hindwings are yellowish-grey. The thorax and first few abdominal segments bear dorsal crests. The sexes are similar, except that the male's antennae are slightly ciliate and those of the female are simple.

Variation can occur in the depth of shading on the wings.

The moth flies at night, visits flowers, and is attracted to light. During the day it rests among the leaves of the foodplant or among other leaves on or near the ground.

Egg
The eggs are oval in shape and rather blunt at one end. The shells are shiny and longitudinally ribbed. When first laid, they are white, becoming pale orange-brown within twenty-four hours and rose-pink after thirty-six hours. They are laid either singly or in small groups on the underside

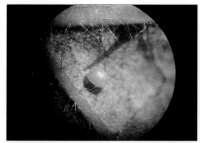

Egg; length 0·75 mm

3rd instar larva; length 9 mm

Fully-grown larva; length 32 mm

Pupa; length 15 mm

Larval home

of bramble leaves, and hatch in about ten days.

Larva

When newly hatched the larva is 1·5 mm long; the head is black and the body deep pink. In the next instars the body is greyish marked with black. When the larva is fully grown, its head and body are reddish-brown, and there are a thin black dorsal line and fine oblique black marks on the sides. On each side of the fourth segment is a round yellowish-white spot. Sometimes a second pair of spots is present.

The eggshell is not eaten. During the first instar, when the body colour is deep pink, the larva feeds on the reddish leaves of the bramble, eating only the cuticle. During the last two instars the larva makes a home for itself by drawing together the edges of a leaf. When it is at rest, its rear claspers are not kept in contact with the leaf, but are raised. It feeds at night.

Pupa

The pupa is dark blackish-brown, slightly lighter between the segments. The surface is dull and roughened, and there is a prominent anal spike. The pupa is enclosed in an open brownish cocoon spun in the litter on the surface of the ground, or just beneath it.

THYATIRIDAE **Yellow Horned**

Wingspan 40–44 mm

IMAGO
EGG
LARVA
PUPA

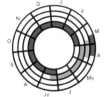

Distribution
England, Wales, and Scotland.

Habitat
Heathland, moorland, and woodland.

Life cycle
One generation a year. Overwinters as a pupa.

Larval foodplant
Birch (*Betula* spp.).

Imago

There are two distinct races of the Yellow Horned: *A. flavicornis galbanus* is found in England and Wales. The forewings are pale greenish-grey crossed by black transverse lines, and with a greenish-grey orbicular stigma. The hindwings are pale grey with slightly darker bands.

A. flavicornis scotica is found in Scotland. The ground colour is much darker and less greenish than the southern race, the forewing markings are more distinct, and individuals are larger.

In both races there is a thoracic crest, and the antennae are reddish-ochreous and shortly ciliate, and also thickened, though less so in the female.

The moth becomes active at dusk, visits sallow blossom, and is attracted to light. During the day it often rests on birch twigs or branches. Favoured habitats are those with areas of small regenerating birch.

Egg; length 1 mm

Larva in May; length 29 mm

Fully-grown larva; length 35 mm

Pupa; length 15 mm

Larval home

Egg

The eggs are roundish-oval in shape, rather shiny, with a strongly reticulated surface. They are white when laid, becoming yellow after two days and rose-pink after four days. They are laid singly or in pairs, tucked beneath a bud, between catkins, or in the fork of a twig. They hatch in about two weeks.

Larva

When newly hatched the larva is 1·5 mm long, with a black head and collar. The body is dark ochreous with scattered short hairs. After feeding the body takes on a greenish tinge. In the following instars the head is brown, and the body is black with white along the sides, on the ventral surface and dotted on the dorsal surface. When the larva is fully grown, its head is brown, and its body pale grey-green, marked with white spots, small black patches, and a thin pale dorsal line.

The eggshell is not eaten. The larva makes a home for itself by spinning leaves together. When young it rolls a single leaf, but as it grows it either folds a leaf over or spins two together. When very young it feeds on the cuticle, and then it begins to eat small holes through the leaf; when older it eats the whole substance of the leaf. It feeds at night, and may be found on small, young birches.

Pupa

The pupa is reddish-brown, darker between the segments. Its surface is dull and rough, and it has a long anal spike. It is enclosed in a thin cocoon spun among the leaves or in the litter beneath the foodplant.

♂ wingspan 35–40 mm

♀ wingspan 35–40 mm

IMAGO
EGG
LARVA
PUPA

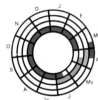

Distribution
England, Wales, and Scotland.

Habitat
Open areas in and around birch woods, and on heaths, near birches.

Life cycle
One generation a year. Over-winters as a pupa.

Larval foodplant
Birch (*Betula* spp.).

Imago
The forewings are dark reddish-brown marked with a few cream-coloured patches which are more extensive in the female, and the hindwings are deep orange marked with blackish-grey. The thorax and abdomen are blackish-brown. The antennae of the male are finely serrate, and those of the female simple.

Variation can occur in the size of the white markings on the forewing and the dark markings on the hindwing, and in the shade of the ground colour.

Very similar in appearance to the Light Orange Underwing (*A. notha*), the Orange Underwing is slightly larger, has more extensive creamy markings, and the dark border on the underside of the hindwing is more broken. The Light Orange Underwing is confined to southern England.

The Orange Underwing is a day-flying species, active in sunshine, when it may be seen flying high round birches, or crossing open areas in their vicinity. Sometimes it settles on bare ground, and it has been recorded feeding at sallow blossom. It will fly in quite a strong wind, and will cover large areas, flying from one group of birches to another. After emergence, the female walks up the trunk of the birch, stopping frequently to 'call'.

Egg
The eggs are oblong in shape with a faint pattern of reticulations, and they are often covered with scales from the female's abdomen. When first laid they are pale olive-green, but this gradually changes to a more ochreous-green. They are usually laid singly or in pairs in the forks of twigs, but sometimes are deposited in small groups against a leaf scar or bump on a twig. They hatch in about two weeks.

Larva
When newly hatched the larva is 1·75 mm long. The head and a narrow collar behind it are brown, and the body is ochreous with numerous short

Eggs on birch twig

Eggs; length 1 mm

3rd instar larva; length 12 mm

4th instar larva; length 22 mm

Fully-grown larva; length 30 mm

Pupa; length 15 mm

bristles. After feeding, the body becomes greenish. During the second instar its colour is pale green, in the third instar dark olive green. In both instars whitish stripes are evident, and these become very pronounced from the fourth instar onwards. Fully grown, the larva is green, marked with white and yellowish-white stripes and white dots. The head is pale green.

The eggshell is not eaten. During the first instar, the larva eats small holes in the leaves, but thereafter it feeds from the edges of the leaves, spinning copious amounts of silk which it uses as a base on which to rest. It feeds by day or night, and the cast larval skins are eaten. If disturbed, it drops from the leaf and hangs by a silken thread.

Pupa
The pupa is very dark reddish-brown in colour, with a shiny, slightly roughened surface. The anal extremity is very blunt, with two short spines each set at right angles to the abdomen. The pupa is formed inside a cocoon woven from a few threads of whitish silk, usually in a crevice of the birch bark, or in litter on the ground, and it overwinters.

Breeding
In captivity, it is necessary to provide the fully-grown larva with either rotten wood or deeply creviced bark in which to pupate.

GEOMETRIDAE (OENOCHROMINAE) **March Moth**

♂ wingspan 35–38 mm

♀ body length 8–10 mm

IMAGO
EGG
LARVA
PUPA

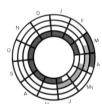

Distribution
Throughout the British Isles, with the exception of northern Scotland.

Habitat
Woodlands, hedgerows, gardens, and orchards.

Life cycle
One generation a year. Over-winters as a pupa.

Larval foodplants
Many deciduous trees and shrubs, including oak (*Quercus* spp.), birch (*Betula* spp.), hawthorn (*Crataegus monogyna*), blackthorn (*Prunus spinosa*), hazel (*Corylus avellana*), plum (*Prunus* spp.), and rose (*Rosa* spp.).

Imago
The forewings of the male are very pointed; the ground colour is greyish-brown, and a zig-zag area across the wing is edged with cream. The hindwings are pale grey-brown with a dark brown discal spot. The antennae are slightly pectinate. The female is wingless, the antennae are simple, and the body is brown with a conspicuous anal tuft.

Variation sometimes occurs in the ground colour of the male's forewings – they may be darker, or in some cases ochreous-brown.

When at rest, the wings of the male are noticeably rolled round the body. Both sexes become active at dusk, when the female climbs up stems or trunks of the foodplant and gives off pheromones to attract the males. Egg laying commences soon after pairing.

Egg
The eggs are oblong, and golden-brown in colour. The tops are very smooth and shiny, and the sides bear a very fine, faint reticulation. They are laid in batches round the twigs and are completely covered with wavy hairs from the female's anal tuft. They hatch in five to six weeks.

Egg batch on oak twig; length 6 mm

Eggs; width 0·5 mm

Fully-grown larva; length 22 mm

Pupa; length 9 mm

Larva

When newly hatched the larva is 2·5 mm long, with a head and body of yellowish-ochreous and a dark dorsal line. When it is fully grown, the head and body are pale green and there are a dark green dorsal stripe, a number of pale yellow subdorsal stripes, and a deeper yellow spiracular stripe; the segmental divisions are pale yellow. The March Moth larva may be distinguished from other similar Geometrid larvae by its possession of a vestigial third pair of prolegs.

The eggshell is not eaten. The larva feeds mainly at night, and during the day rests on the undersides of leaves.

Pupa

The pupa is dumpy in shape, smooth, and shiny. It is olive green in colour, with the last abdominal segment orange, dark eyes, and brown antennae cases. It is enclosed in a very dense, tough oval cocoon of brown silk covered with soil particles, situated beneath the surface of the ground below the foodplant.

GEOMETRIDAE (GEOMETRINAE) **Large Emerald**

Wingspan 50–64 mm

IMAGO
EGG
LARVA
PUPA

Distribution
Throughout the British Isles.

Habitat
Woodland and heathland.

Life cycle
One generation a year. Over-winters as a young larva.

Larval foodplant
Birch (*Betula* spp.). Also recorded on hazel (*Corylus avellana*), beech (*Fagus sylvatica*), and alder (*Alnus glutinosa*).

Imago
The wings are green, marked with faint white wavy lines and spots. The head and thorax are green, and the antennae and abdomen whitish. The sexes are similar, but the antennae of the male are ciliate and those of the female are simple.

Variation may occur in the shade of green, or in the number of white lines.

The moth flies at night, beginning after dark, and is attracted to light.

Egg
The eggs are oval with a depression on the upper surface, and the shells are rather rough in appearance. When first laid they are creamy-white; after

Eggs on birch leaf

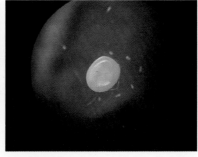

Egg; length 1 mm

Larva in spring; length 12 mm

Larva in May; length 20 mm

Fully-grown larva; length 29 mm

Pupa; length 19 mm

a few days they become greenish-yellow, and eventually are tinged with pink. They are laid singly or in pairs on leaves of the foodplant, usually on the underside, and hatch in about two weeks.

Larva

The newly-hatched larva is 2·5 mm long, and very dark brown, with a paler brown head. Before hibernation the middle segments of the body are green and the rest of the body and the head reddish-brown. During hibernation the whole larva is dark reddish-brown. When feeding recommences in the spring, the larva is a mixture of green and reddish-brown. When fully grown it is green with a yellow spiracular line and a series of red-tipped dorsal humps; the last segment and anal claspers are reddish-brown.

The eggshell is not eaten. The larva begins hibernation at the beginning of September, resting on a pad of silk on a twig, and its colour exactly matches that of the twig. It begins feeding again towards the end of April, and gradually becomes more variegated with green. It is a night feeder, and during the day rests among leaves near the tips of the foodplant twigs.

Pupa

The pupa is smooth with a dull surface. It is pale green in colour, with darker green between the segments, pale brown wingcases, a broken dorsal line of brownish marks, and a reddish anal tip. It is enclosed in a flimsy cocoon of whitish silk in litter on the ground, and the adult emerges in three to four weeks.

GEOMETRIDAE (GEOMETRINAE) **Small Emerald**

Wingspan 35–40 mm

IMAGO
EGG
LARVA
PUPA

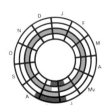

Distribution
Most of England, commonest in the southern half; Wales.

Habitat
Hedgerows, downland, and woodland edges. Mainly on chalk.

Life cycle
One generation a year. Overwinters as a young larva.

Larval foodplant
Traveller's-joy (*Clematis vitalba*).

Imago
The wings are a very pale delicate green; the forewings have two white lines and the hindwings one. The head, thorax and abdomen are pale green and the antennae white. Sexes are similar, but the male's antennae are ciliate and the female's are simple.

Variation can occur in the shade of green and the prominence of the white lines.

The moth flies at night, commencing at dusk, and is sometimes attracted to light.

Egg
The eggs are yellowish-green, smooth and shiny.

Hemistola chrysoprasaria (ESPER)

Eggs on traveller's-joy

Eggs; width 0·75 mm

Larva hibernating; length 9 mm

Larva in May; length 16 mm

Fully-grown larva; length 29 mm

Pupa; length 15 mm

They are lozenge-shaped – circular and flattened on the upper and lower surfaces – and when laid piled carefully one on top of another in a column they bear an uncanny resemblance to a short tendril of the foodplant. They hatch in about ten days, and just before the event the dark head of the larva is visible through the side of the egg.

Larva

When newly hatched the larva is 2 mm long, and is greenish-yellow with a brown head. During hibernation it is light brown, and after feeding recommences its colour becomes reddish-green. When fully grown, its body is yellowish-green with whitish dorsal and lateral stripes. The crown of its head is deeply notched with reddish-brown points.

The eggshell is not eaten. Hibernation begins towards the end of September, the larva resting on a silk pad on a stem of the foodplant, which it resembles very closely. Feeding begins again in May. If disturbed, the larva falls to the ground with its body held straight and rigid. It feeds at night and during the day rests on stems of the foodplant.

Pupa

The pupa is pale green, marked with darker green longitudinal lines. The surface is smooth and not shiny. The anal point and the curved spines on this point are reddish. The pupa is enclosed in a loose cocoon spun among leaves of the larval foodplant and the adult emerges in about two weeks.

GEOMETRIDAE (STERRHINAE) **Clay Triple-lines**

Wingspan 26–32 mm

IMAGO
EGG
LARVA
PUPA

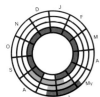

Distribution
England and Wales, as far north as Cheshire and Lincolnshire but commonest in southern England. Local in parts of Ireland.

Habitat
Woodland containing beech.

Life cycle
Usually one generation a year, but sometimes a partial second generation, especially in the south, producing adult moths from mid-August to mid-October. Overwinters as a pupa.

Larval foodplant
Beech (*Fagus sylvatica*).

Imago
The ground colour of the wings is reddish-ochreous, with three brown transverse lines, of which the central line is solid and well defined and the other two are broken and dotted. There are white discal spots on each wing, those on the hindwings being the more distinct. The sexes are similar, differing only in the antennae – those of the male are pectinate and those of the female are simple.

Variation occurs in the ground colour of the wings, which can range from yellowish-ochreous to reddish-ochreous, and in the intensity of the transverse lines, one or more of which may be very faint, or even missing. Occasionally the discal spots are very faint, or absent altogether.

The moth flies at night, becoming active at dusk, and is attracted to light.

Eggs on beech; length 1 mm

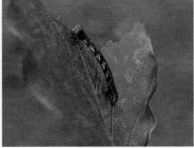

Half-grown larva; length 17 mm

Fully-grown larva (green form); length 21 mm

Fully-grown larva (brown form); length 23 mm

Pupa (green form); length 12·5 mm

Pupa (brown form); length 12·5 mm

Egg

The eggs are oblong-oval in shape, with a shiny, finely pitted surface. When newly laid they are white, but after about four days an irregular pattern of reddish blotches develops. They are laid either singly or in pairs among the fine hairs on the edge of a beech leaf, and hatch in ten to twelve days.

Larva

When newly hatched the larva is 2 mm long; the head is brownish-ochreous, and the body ochreous, with a series of brown chevrons along the back which extend down the sides. When half grown, its head is reddish-brown and its body darker brown with oblique yellow lateral dashes edged above with blackish-brown. When the larva is fully grown there are two colour forms: in the first the head is reddish-brown and the body brown with the dark-edged yellowish lateral marks now much fainter; in the second the head is reddish-brown and the body pale green with very faint yellow lateral marks. There are two pairs of prolegs, which in the green form of the larva are pale pink.

The eggshell is not eaten. During the early instars the larva eats only the cuticle of the leaf – the resulting pattern on the leaf is conspicuous and distinctive. If disturbed, the larva hangs on a silken thread. It feeds at night, and during the day rests stretched out on a twig or the back of a leaf.

Pupa

The pupa has a somewhat shiny, roughened surface. It tapers sharply towards the anal point, and at the head end there are two blunt ear-like projections. There are two colour forms: in the first the ground colour is green; in the second it is brownish-ochreous with darker brown speckles and pink segmental divisions. In both forms there is a dark-edged white line bordering the wing-cases, pink 'ears', and a pink stripe on the dorsal surface of the anal spike. The pupa is attached by tail hooks and a silken girdle to the underside of a beech leaf.

GEOMETRIDAE (LARENTIINAE) **Garden Carpet**

Wingspan 26–31 mm

IMAGO
EGG
LARVA
PUPA

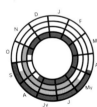

Distribution
Throughout the British Isles.

Habitat
Gardens, hedgerows, and waste ground.

Life cycle
Usually two generations a year, but occasionally a partial third generation in southern England. Overwinters as a pupa.

Larval foodplants
Cruciferous plants, such as cultivated cabbage and Brussels sprouts, arabis, wallflowers, and garlic mustard (*Alliaria petiolata*).

Imago
The fore- and hindwings are grey, marked with grey-brown wavy lines; the forewings in addition have dark grey-brown blotches. The head and thorax are grey-brown, and the abdomen grey marked with dark grey-brown spots. The sexes are similar, except that the male's antennae are ciliate and the female's simple.

Variation is frequent, both in the size of the moth, and the pattern on the wings, which varies in extent and intensity. In some cases the ground colour may be almost white. Melanic specimens sometimes occur, especially in northern Scotland (f. *thules*).

The moth is particularly abundant in gardens. It begins flying at dusk, and frequently comes to light. During the day it can be found resting on tree trunks, walls, and fences, and sometimes on

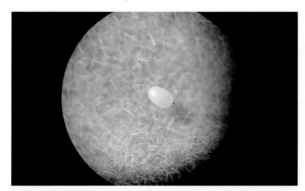

Egg; length 0·8 mm

Fully-grown larva (green form); length 23 mm

Fully-grown larva (brown form); length 24 mm

Pupa; length 9 mm

leaves. The two or three generations a year mean that adults may be seen at any time between April and October.

Egg

The egg is oval, slightly flattened, and somewhat tapered at one end. The surface is slightly pitted and shiny. It is pale yellowish-white until just before the emergence of the larva, when it turns black. Eggs are laid singly on the underside of a leaf of the foodplant, and hatch in about ten days.

Larva

When newly hatched the larva is 3 mm long, and ochreous, with a brown head. The colour of the fully grown larva is very variable – it may be green, grey or brown. There is a pale lateral stripe.

On the dorsal surface is a series of dark spots arranged in diamond patterns.

The eggshell is not eaten. The larva feeds at night, and during the day rests concealed in the foodplant foliage.

Pupa

The pupa is smooth, shiny, and reddish-brown in colour with a slight greenish tinge on the wing-cases. It is attached to the cocoon by means of a long, slightly curved tail spike. The cocoon is usually formed beneath the surface of the soil, but may be found occasionally in leaf litter beneath the foodplant. The adult moth emerges in about eight weeks, except in those individuals where the pupa overwinters.

GEOMETRIDAE (LARENTIINAE) **Shoulder Stripe**

Wingspan 31–35 mm

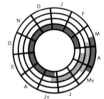

IMAGO
EGG
LARVA
PUPA

Distribution
Throughout the British Isles.

Habitat
Hedgerows, open woodland, downland, and bushy places.

Life cycle
One generation a year. Over-winters as a pupa.

Larval foodplant
Wild rose (*Rosa* spp.).

Imago
The forewings have transverse bands of brown and cream. The hindwings, which have a scalloped margin, are greyish-brown shaded with brown, and with a dark brown shading at the margin. The body is marked with shades of brown, and the abdomen bears two dark spots on the dorsal surface of each segment. The sexes are similar, except that the male's antennae are serrate and the female's simple.

Variation occurs frequently in the extent and colour of the bands on the forewings, some individuals being much darker than others.

The moth begins flying at dusk, visits flowers, and comes to light.

Egg
The eggs are oval, slightly flattened, and tapered at one end. The surface is shiny and delicately pitted. They are primrose yellow when laid, becoming orange after a few days. The eggs are laid singly on the edges of the foodplant leaves, usually on the upper surface, but sometimes on thorns or stems. They hatch in about ten days.

Larva
When newly hatched the larva is 2 mm in length, and the head and body are yellowish-ochreous.

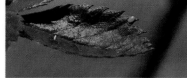

Egg on rose leaf

Egg; length 0·75 mm

Pupa; length 11 mm

Fully-grown larva; length 27 mm

Until the penultimate instar the colour of the body is green, darker along the back. The spiracles are large and black, and the head orange. When the larva is fully grown, its body is pale green with yellow between the segments. It has a purple spiracular stripe, and its prolegs are purple. Its spiracles are black and its head orange.

The eggshell is not eaten. The larva feeds at night, and if disturbed falls to the ground and rolls itself into a knot.

Pupa

The pupa is very dark brown, and shiny, with a slightly roughened surface. It is enclosed in a thin cocoon formed in leaf litter on the surface of the ground beneath the foodplant.

GEOMETRIDAE (LARENTIINAE) **Winter Moth**

♂ wingspan 28–32 mm

♀ body length 8 mm

IMAGO
EGG
LARVA
PUPA

Distribution
Throughout the British Isles.

Habitat
Hedgerows, woodlands, gardens, and orchards.

Life cycle
One generation a year. Over-winters as an egg.

Larval foodplants
Most deciduous trees and shrubs. Often on garden fruit trees.

Imago
The forewings of the male are grey-brown, shaded with brown and marked with fine wavy lines. The hindwings are pale grey-brown. The wings of the female are reduced to short stumps and are useless for flying.

Variation can occur in the wing ground colour or in the line markings on the forewings of the male.

Both sexes become active soon after dusk. The males often come to light. Females run up the trunks and stems of trees and bushes, attracting the males by means of pheromones.

Egg
The eggs are oval, flattened, and have a finely pitted surface. When laid they are greenish in colour, but they change gradually to a brownish-orange. They are laid singly or in small groups, tucked into crevices in bark, and, having over-wintered, they normally hatch about the beginning of April.

Larva
Immediately after hatching, the larva measures 1·5 mm in length, and its head and body are dark grey. When fully grown, its head is yellowish-green and its body pale green with yellow between the segments. It has a dark green dorsal line, two pairs of whitish subdorsal lines, and a

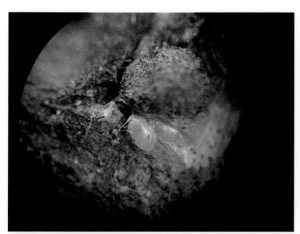

Eggs; length 0·5 mm

Larval home

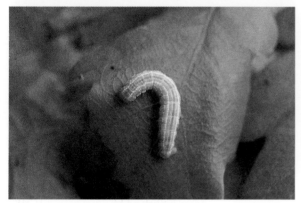

Fully-grown larva; length 15 mm

Pupa; length 9 mm

yellow spiracular line.

The eggshell is not eaten. When very small, the larva hangs suspended by a silken thread, but by the end of the second instar it makes a home for itself by spinning together adjacent leaves, or by folding over one leaf. It rests inside the shelter in a characteristic attitude, with the head and front portion of the body bent round to one side. Large numbers of these larvae sometimes cause great damage to fruit trees in orchards.

Pupa
The pupa is smooth, shiny, and light brown in colour, with a greenish tinge. It is enclosed in an earthen cocoon just beneath the surface of the soil.

GEOMETRIDAE (LARENTIINAE) **Foxglove Pug**

Wingspan 18–22 mm

IMAGO
EGG
LARVA
PUPA

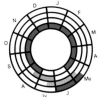

Distribution
Throughout the British Isles.

Habitat
Downland, woodland, heathland, and sea-cliffs – wherever foxgloves grow.

Life cycle
One generation a year. Over-winters as a pupa.

Larval foodplant
Foxglove (*Digitalis purpurea*).

Imago
The forewings are transversed by wavy bands of blackish-grey, white, and reddish-brown. The hindwings are pale grey with faint darker and lighter bands. The thorax is reddish-brown, and the abdomen grey with a black band on the second segment and black dots along the dorsal surface. The sexes are similar, except that the antennae of the male are finely ciliate and those of the female are simple.

Variation can occur in the colour of the shading on the forewings. The subspecies *hebudium*, which is found in the Hebrides and western Wales, lacks the reddish-brown colour on the forewings and is therefore much greyer in appearance.

The moth flies at night, comes to light, and during the day may be found resting on tree trunks or wooden posts, occasionally on the underside of a foxglove leaf.

Egg
The egg is oval and shiny, with a finely pitted

Eggs on foxglove

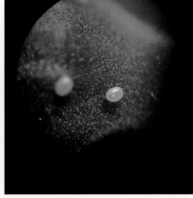

Egg; length 0·8 mm

Larval home

Fully-grown larva; length 15 mm

Pupa; length 7 mm

surface. It is creamy-white when laid, but becomes duller just before hatching. Eggs are laid singly or in pairs on the calyx or the base of the corolla of the foxglove. They hatch in seven to ten days.

Larva
When newly hatched, the larva is 1·75 mm long and ochreous in colour, with a dark brown head. When fully grown, its body can be very variable in colour, though it is usually some shade of dull green with darker green lines. The head and spiracles are black.

The eggshell is not eaten. The larva enters the corolla of the foxglove, fastens the mouth of the flower together with silk, and lives inside, feeding on the stamens. Tenanted flowers are quite conspicuous, owing to the closed mouth, and to the fact that they remain on the stem after those around them have fallen off.

Pupa
The pupa is reddish-brown and shiny. The thorax and wingcases are smooth, and the abdomen slightly roughened with a dark brown tip. The thin cocoon is formed just beneath the surface of the soil.

GEOMETRIDAE (LARENTIINAE) **Netted Pug**

Wingspan 20–24 mm

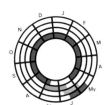

Distribution
England, Wales and north-eastern Scotland.

Habitat
Chalk and limestone districts, and coastal cliffs.

Life cycle
One generation a year. Overwinters as a pupa, sometimes twice.

Larval foodplants
Bladder campion (*Silene vulgaris*). In coastal districts, sea campion (*S. maritima*).

Imago
The wings are pale grey. The forewings are crossed by three or four zig-zag black-and-white lines; the hindwings are less boldly marked. The head and body are pale grey, the abdomen with a few black dots and a black belt on the second segment. The sexes are similar, although the male's antennae are finely ciliate and the female's are simple.

The subspecies *fumosae*, *ochracae*, and *hebridensis*, which occur in the northern isles, have a darker ground colour than the mainland subspecies *venosata*.

The moth begins flying at dusk, and sometimes comes to light.

Egg
The eggs are oval and slightly flattened, with a very shiny, finely reticulated surface. They are creamy-white, becoming slightly more yellowish before hatching. They are laid singly or in pairs on the calyces of the foodplant, and hatch in seven or eight days.

Eggs on bladder campion

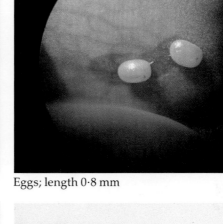

Eggs; length 0·8 mm

Fully-grown larva; length 13 mm

Pupa; length 8·5 mm

Larva

When newly hatched, the larva is 1·75 mm long and dark grey in colour, with a black head. When fully grown, its head is shining black and there is a black collar just behind it. Its body is dark grey, though paler on the sides.

The eggshell is not eaten. The larva burrows inside the calyces of the campion and lives therein, feeding on the developing seeds.

Pupa

The pupa is pale reddish-brown with a dark brown tip to the abdomen. It is shiny with a roughened surface. It is enclosed in a slight cocoon situated just beneath the surface of the ground, and may sometimes overwinter twice.

GEOMETRIDAE (ENNOMINAE) **The Magpie**

Wingspan 42–48 mm

IMAGO
EGG
LARVA
PUPA

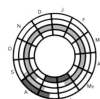

Distribution
Throughout the British Isles.

Habitat
Gardens, woodland, hedgerows, and waste ground.

Life cycle
One generation a year. Over-winters as a young larva.

Larval foodplants
Currants and gooseberry (*Ribes* spp.), hawthorn (*Crataegus mono-gyna*), blackthorn (*Prunus spinosa*), hazel (*Corylus avellana*), *Euonymus* spp., and various other shrubs and plants. In parts of Scotland it is recorded on heather (*Calluna vulgaris*).

Imago
The ground colour of the wings is white. The forewings have a pattern of black spots and yellow bands, and the hindwings bear black spots. The head is black, and the thorax and abdomen yellow with black spots. Sexes are similar, but the antennae of the male are ciliate while those of the female are simple.

This is an extremely variable species, mainly in the amount of black on the wings. Striking aberrations are quite scarce among wild specimens – they are usually obtained in captivity by selective breeding of individuals from the wild with slight variations.

Although it will sometimes fly during the day, The Magpie is normally a night-flyer, and it is attracted to light.

Egg
The eggs are oval with a finely reticulated surface.

Egg batch

Eggs; length 1·5 mm

Fully-grown larva; length 25 mm

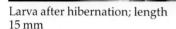

Larva after hibernation; length 15 mm

Pupa; length 15 mm

Creamy-white in colour, they become blue-black just before hatching. They are laid in batches on the underside of leaves of the foodplant, and hatch in two to three weeks.

Larva

When newly hatched, the larva is 2·5 mm long, with black head and yellowish-ochreous body. When fully grown, its white body, marked with black spots and a reddish-orange lateral stripe, bears a few short black hairs; the head and legs are also black.

The eggshell is not eaten. During the first and second instars the larva hangs by a silken thread.

It hibernates when small, and recommences feeding in March or April. If disturbed, it drops from the foodplant and lies motionless in a tight 'U' shape. Large numbers of these larvae can cause severe damage to currant and gooseberry bushes.

Pupa

The pupa is smooth and shiny. It is black with seven yellow bands on the abdomen. The cremaster bears prominent hooks by which the pupa is attached to the cocoon. This flimsy, transparent structure is situated under a leaf, among stems, or beneath a ledge, for example on a fence. The adult moth emerges in about three weeks.

GEOMETRIDAE (ENNOMINAE) **Brimstone Moth**

Wingspan 32–45 mm

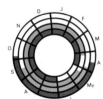

IMAGO ■
EGG ■
LARVA ■
PUPA ■

Distribution
Throughout the British Isles.

Habitat
Woodland, hedgerows, bushy places, and gardens.

Life cycle
In the north of Britain there is one generation a year, and the moth is on the wing in June and July. In southern districts there are over-lapping generations, so that adult moths and other stages may all be seen at any time from about mid-April to the beginning of October. Overwinters as either a larva or a pupa.

Larval foodplants
Various trees and shrubs including hawthorn (*Crataegus monogyna*), blackthorn (*Prunus spinosa*), apple (*Malus* spp.), plum (*Prunus* spp.), hazel (*Corylus avellana*), and rowan (*Sorbus aucuparia*).

Imago
The wings are bright sulphur-yellow with a few faint grey-brown marks. The forewings have several rusty-red marks along the costa, and the discal spot is white edged with dark red-brown. There are smaller similar discal spots on the hind-wings. The head, thorax and abdomen are yellow. The antennae are shortly ciliate in the male and simple in the female.

Variation can occur in the shade of the ground colour, and the extent of the reddish costal marks, which sometimes extend to form a continuous streak.

The moth flies from dusk onwards, and is attracted to light. During the day it can often be disturbed from vegetation.

Eggs; length 1 mm

Pupa; length 13 mm

Fully-grown larva; length 27 mm

Egg

The eggs are oval, flattened on the upper surface, and shiny. When first laid they are white, and after three or four days they develop a pattern of small orange blotches. They are laid either singly or in short rows, usually on the upper surface of a leaf of the foodplant, and hatch in about twelve days.

Larva

When newly hatched the larva is 2 mm long and dark ochreous in colour, with a brown head. By the third instar its dorsal surface is brown and its sides ochreous. When fully grown its head is light brown, and its body either brownish-grey or greenish, with two prominent dorsal bumps on the sixth segment. It has two extra pairs of very rudimentary prolegs.

The eggshell is not eaten. The larva feeds at night, and during the day rests on twigs, well camouflaged by its stick-like appearance.

Pupa

The pupa is smooth and greenish-brown in colour, with a darker dorsal stripe and darker veins on the wingcases. It is attached to the inside of the cocoon by tail spines. The cocoon consists of dense white silk, and is spun among leaves and in litter on the surface of the ground beneath the foodplant. In individuals that do not overwinter, the adult moth emerges in about ten days.

GEOMETRIDAE (ENNOMINAE) **Early Thorn**

♂ (spring); wingspan 46–50 mm

♀ (summer); wingspan 38–44 mm

IMAGO
EGG
LARVA
PUPA

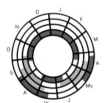

Distribution
Throughout the British Isles, but less common in Scotland.

Habitat
Woodland and hedgerows.

Life cycle
Two generations a year, except in northern Britain where there is only one, which produces moths in May and June. Overwinters as a pupa.

Larval foodplants
A wide variety of trees and shrubs including sallow (*Salix* spp.), birch (*Betula* spp.), hawthorn (*Crataegus monogyna*), blackthorn (*Prunus spinosa*), and bramble (*Rubus fruticosus*).

Imago
In the spring generation, the wings of the male are pale reddish-brown, marked and speckled with darker brown, and with dark brown transverse lines. The female is similarly marked, but the ground colour is browner and the margins of the hindwings are more deeply dentated. The antennae of the male are pectinate and those of the female serrate. Individuals of the summer generation are usually smaller and paler in colour than those of the first generation.

Variation can occur in the shade of the ground colour, which may sometimes be very dark.

The moth flies at night, first becoming active at dusk, and is attracted to light. When at rest the wings are held vertically over the back in the manner of a butterfly.

Egg
The eggs are roundish-oval in shape, with a finely pitted surface. They are greenish-yellow when laid, but after two days become rose pink. They are laid singly, in pairs, or in small groups, usually on the underside of a leaf of the foodplant. They hatch in about ten days.

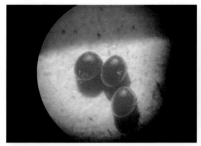

Eggs; length 1 mm

Larva in August; length 15 mm

Fully-grown larva; length 38 mm

Pupa; length 15 mm

Cocoon

Larva

When newly hatched, the larva is 2·5 mm long, dark red-brown with transverse white bands. By the third instar the body is reddish-brown. When fully grown, the body is dark reddish-brown with a pair of raised points on the back of the seventh and eighth segments. The third pair of true legs are much longer than the other two pairs.

The eggshell is not eaten. When about half grown, the larva rests with its head thrown back at right angles to the body; when fully grown the head is kept in line with the body. At all stages the resemblance of the larva to a twig is quite remarkable.

Pupa

The pupa is dark reddish-brown with darker wingcases, smooth and very shiny. The larval skin is retained. The pupa is contained in a thin cocoon of whitish silk spun either among leaves of the foodplant, or in litter beneath it.

GEOMETRIDAE (ENNOMINAE) **Feathered Thorn**

Wingspan 46–50 mm

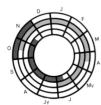

IMAGO
EGG
LARVA
PUPA

Distribution
Throughout the British Isles.

Habitat
Woodland, bushy places, hedgerows, and heathland.

Life cycle
One generation a year. Overwinters as an egg.

Larval foodplants
A wide variety of trees and shrubs, including birch (*Betula* spp.), sallow (*Salix* spp.), oak (*Quercus* spp.), blackthorn (*Prunus spinosa*), hawthorn (*Crataegus monogyna*), and poplar (*Populus* spp.).

Imago
The wings are reddish-brown, finely freckled with dark brown scales. There are dark brown transverse lines and a white apical spot on the forewings. The sexes are similar, but the antennae of the male are plumose and those of the female are shortly pectinate.

Variation occurs very frequently in the ground colour and the position of the transverse lines.

The moth is a night-flyer, commencing its flight at dusk; the male is the more active sex. The English name of the species refers to the male's large feathery antennae.

Egg
The eggs are shiny, with a very finely pitted surface, and are rather cylindrical in shape. They are greenish in colour, becoming purplish-brown

Eggs; width 0·5 mm

Larva in May; length 20 mm

Fully-grown larva; length 50 mm

Pupa; length 18 mm

before hatching. They are laid standing on their ends in batches on twigs of the foodplant, and, having overwintered, usually hatch during April.

Larva

When newly hatched the larva is 2 mm long and blackish-grey in colour. When it is half grown its head is reddish-brown, its sides pale brown and its back purplish; its spiracles are yellow, and there are two raised points on the twelfth segment. When fully grown, its head is reddish-brown, and its body variable in colour, but usually some shade of brown; there is a faint yellowish subdorsal line on the first three segments, and the raised points near the rear claspers have red tips.

The eggshell is not eaten. The larva feeds at night, during the day rests on twigs or stems of the foodplant, and is extremely well camouflaged.

Pupa

The pupa is reddish-brown with darker wing-cases, smooth and very shiny. It is enclosed in a very tough cocoon just below the surface of the ground. The larva remains in the cocoon for several weeks before pupating.

GEOMETRIDAE (ENNOMINAE) **Mottled Umber**

♂ wingspan 40–45 mm

♂

Distribution
Throughout the British Isles.

Habitat
Woodland, hedgerows and bushy places.

Life cycle
One generation a year. Over-winters as an egg.

Larval foodplants
A very wide range of trees and shrubs, particularly oak (*Quercus* spp.), birch (*Betula* spp.), sallow (*Salix* spp.), blackthorn (*Prunus spinosa*), hawthorn (*Crataegus monogyna*), and hazel (*Corylus avellana*).

Imago
The wings of the male are ochreous-brown, speckled with darker brown, and with dark brown discal spots. The forewings are crossed by two darker bands. The antennae are pectinate. The female is wingless; her body is pale ochreous-brown with darker brown shading and two rows of dark spots along the back, and her antennae are simple.

Variation occurs very frequently in the ground colour and extent of the markings on the wings of the male.

Both sexes become active at dusk, and the males are attracted to light. Females may be found on the trunks and stems of the foodplants, which they climb after dark.

Egg
The eggs are longish-oval in shape, shiny, and appear smooth, but a very slight surface reticulation is visible under high magnification. When laid the colour is pale pinkish-orange, but this darkens slightly after seven to ten days. The eggs are laid either singly or in small batches tucked in among the buds of the foodplants, or in bark crevices, and, having overwintered, they usually hatch during April.

Larva
When newly hatched, the larva is 2 mm long, the

♀ body length 13 mm

Eggs; length 0·8 mm

Fully-grown larva (green form); length 25 mm

Fully-grown larva (brown form); length 27 mm

Pupae; length ♂ 11 mm, ♀ 16 mm

head is ochreous, the body dark olive green dorsally with a greenish-ochreous spiracular stripe. When the larva is fully grown, the head is brown, the body either grey-green or reddish-brown with reddish dorsal patches; along the side is a wavy black line below which is a series of yellow patches tinged with red.

The eggshell is not eaten. If disturbed, the larva drops from the foodplant and hangs suspended on a silken thread. Large numbers of these larvae can cause severe damage to trees, thereby living up to their name *'defoliaria'*.

Pupa

The pupa is reddish-brown and shiny, with a finely pitted surface and a long tail spike. It is formed either in litter on the ground or just beneath the surface of the soil.

GEOMETRIDAE (ENNOMINAE) **Common Heath**

♂ wingspan 28–34 mm

IMAGO
EGG
LARVA
PUPA

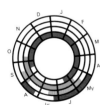

Distribution
Throughout the British Isles.

Habitat
Heathland, moorland, downland and woodland.

Life cycle
Two generations a year. The second generation is partial, and does not always appear in northern districts. Overwinters as a pupa.

Larval foodplants
Heaths (*Erica* spp.), heather (*Calluna vulgaris*), clover (*Trifolium* spp.), and trefoils (*Lotus* spp.).

Imago
The wings of the male are brownish-ochreous, freckled and banded with dark brown and with chequered fringes. The antennae are strongly pectinate. The wings of the female are marked similarly to those of the male, but the ground colour is much whiter. Also, her antennae are simple, and she is smaller.

Variation is very frequent, especially in the male, and may consist of changes in the shade of the ground colour, or in the sharpness and extent of the dark brown bands.

This is a day-flying species, and both sexes may be seen flying in sunshine, or may be readily disturbed from low-growing vegetation on dull days.

♀ wingspan 24–28 mm   Fully-grown larva; length 26 mm   Pupa; length 10·5 mm

Egg; length 1 mm

Half-grown larva; length 11 mm

Egg
The eggs are oval in shape, with a finely pitted surface. They are yellow, laid singly on leaves of the foodplants, and hatch in ten to fourteen days.

Larva
When newly hatched the larva is 1·5 mm long. It is extremely variable in colour, but in the early instars there is a broad dark dorsal stripe, and the sides and ventral area are pale. When it is fully grown the ground colour may be brown, ochreous, green or grey; there are usually faint wavy lines on the back, and the spiracular line may be darker than the ground colour or more yellowish.

The eggshell is not eaten. The larva feeds mainly at night, and rests in a straight position on the foodplant.

Pupa
The pupa is reddish-brown and shiny, with a long tail spike, and a slightly roughened surface. It is formed in a thin earthen cocoon just below the surface of the ground.

GEOMETRIDAE (ENNOMINAE) **Bordered White**

♀ wingspan 35–40 mm

IMAGO ■
EGG ▨
LARVA ▦
PUPA ■

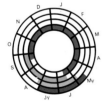

Distribution
Throughout the British Isles, ex-
cept Orkney, Shetland, and the
Outer Hebrides.

Habitat
Coniferous woodland, and heathland in the vicinity of conifers.

Life cycle
One generation a year. Over-
winters as a pupa.

Larval foodplants
Scots pine (*Pinus sylvestris*), and
other species of pine.

Imago
In southern England the ground colour of the

male's wings is pale yellow, while in northern
districts it is white. In both forms the wings are
broadly edged with dark chocolate brown, and the
lighter areas are shaded with this colour. The
antennae are strongly pectinate. Females are similarly marked, but the chocolate brown is much
lighter; in the south the ground colour is orange,
and in the north it is pale brown. The antennae of
the female are simple.

Variation occurs throughout the species' range
in the amount of ground colour present on the
wings.

The Bordered White is mainly a night-flyer,
although it will sometimes fly in sunshine, and
may easily be disturbed during the day from the
branches of the foodplant.

Egg
The eggs are oval and somewhat flattened on the

Eggs on pine

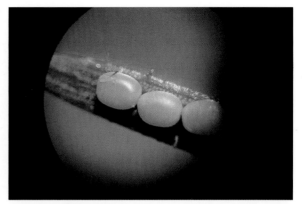

Eggs; length 1 mm

Fully-grown larva; length 24 mm

Pupa; length 14 mm

upper surface. They are pale green, shiny, and faintly reticulated. They are laid in short rows on the upper surface of the pine needles, and hatch in about two weeks.

Larva
When newly hatched the larva is 3 mm long, and green in colour, with a brown head. When it is fully grown, the head is green, and the body green with whitish dorsal and subdorsal lines and a yellow spiracular stripe.

The eggshell is not eaten. When resting among pine needles, the larva is extremely well camouflaged. Large numbers may cause severe damage to trees in conifer plantations.

Pupa
The pupa is blackish-brown, very shiny, and with a slightly roughened surface, especially on the abdomen. It is contained in a slight cocoon formed among fallen pine needles, or in other litter beneath the tree.

SPHINGIDAE (SPHINGINAE) **Pine Hawk-moth**

Wingspan 74–80 mm

IMAGO
EGG
LARVA
PUPA

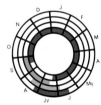

Distribution
Hampshire, Dorset, Surrey, Suffolk and Norfolk.

Habitat
Pine forests and heathland with pine trees.

Life cycle
One generation a year. Overwinters as a pupa, sometimes twice.

Larval foodplants
Scots pine (*Pinus sylvestris*), Norway spruce (*Picea abies*).

Imago
The forewings are dark grey, dusted with white scales and shaded with black. There are three black dashes in the discal area. The hindwings are darker than the forewings. All the wing fringes are chequered black and white. The thorax is dark grey with black stripes, and the abdomen is banded black and white with a blackish dorsal line. The antennae are simple, hooked at the tip, and those of the male are longer than those of the female.

Variation can occur in the shade of the ground colour and the number of dark markings on the wings.

The moth flies at night, beginning at dusk. It visits flowers, from which it feeds while on the wing, and is attracted to light. During the day it rests on tree trunks, usually quite low down.

Eggs on Scots pine

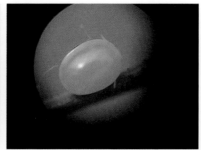

Egg; length 2 mm

Larva before 3rd moult; length
30 mm

Pupa; length 34 mm

Fully-grown larva; length 70 mm

Egg

The eggs are smooth, roundish-oval and shining. They are yellow, becoming grey just before hatching, are laid singly or in groups of two or three on pine needles, and hatch in eight to ten days.

Larva

When newly hatched the larva is 5 mm long, the head is greenish-ochreous marked with dark brown, the body greenish-ochreous, and the horn dark brown. Until after the third moult, the head and body are green with yellow stripes and orange spiracles. When the larva is fully grown the head is reddish-brown marked with black; the body is green with a wide reddish-brown dorsal band, broken yellowish subdorsal and spiracular lines,

and black-ringed orange spiracles; the horn is blackish-brown and rough.

The eggshell is partially eaten. The larva feeds mainly at night, and when not feeding rests among the pine needles, where it is extremely well camouflaged. It may be found most frequently on lower branches. Just before pupation its colouring becomes dull and brownish.

Pupa

The pupa is dark reddish-brown, only slightly shiny, and with a rather roughened surface. The tongue case is prominent but short. The pupa is formed just beneath the surface of the soil, and may sometimes overwinter twice.

SPHINGIDAE (SPHINGINAE) **Poplar Hawk-moth**

Wingspan 72–90 mm

IMAGO
EGG
LARVA
PUPA

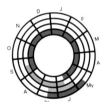

Distribution
Throughout the British Isles.

Habitat
Open woodland, parkland, and damp areas where the foodplants grow.

Life cycle
Usually one generation a year, but occasionally there is a second generation, producing adult moths in late August and September. Overwinters as a pupa.

Larval foodplants
Poplar (*Populus* spp.), aspen (*P. tremula*), and sallows and willows (*Salix* spp.).

Imago
The wings are greyish-brown, shaded with darker brown, and with prominent ochreous veins. There is a white reniform stigma on each forewing. The hindwings have a red basal patch. The antennae of the male are serrate, while those of the female are slimmer and smoother.

Variation can occur in the ground colour which, especially in the female, may be pale buff.

The moth flies at night, becoming active at dusk, and is attracted to light. When at rest its wings closely resemble dead leaves.

Egg
The eggs are roundish-oval, shiny with a smooth appearance, and greenish in colour. They are laid either singly or in pairs on a foodplant leaf, often on the underside, and hatch in about ten days.

Egg; length 2 mm

Larva in August; length 35 mm

Fully-grown larva; length 45 mm

Pupa; length 32 mm

Larva

When newly hatched the larva is 7 mm long, its head and body are pale green, and it has a green horn which is very long in proportion to the size of the larva. When it is fully grown its body is yellowish-green or bluish-green, and very rough, being covered with raised yellow points. There are oblique yellow lateral stripes, and the horn is yellow, often tinged with red. The spiracles are oval, and white in colour, ringed with red. A form of the larva with red subdorsal spots has been recorded.

The eggshell may be partially eaten. The larva normally rests on the underside of a leaf or twig of the foodplant, where its colouring and oblique yellow lateral stripes cause it to blend in with its surroundings.

Pupa

The pupa is blackish-brown and dull, with a rough texture. It is contained in a slight earthen cocoon just beneath the surface of the ground.

SPHINGIDAE (MACROGLOSSINAE) **Small Elephant Hawk-moth**

Wingspan 48–55 mm

IMAGO
EGG
LARVA
PUPA

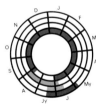

Distribution
Throughout the British Isles, though less widespread in Scotland and Ireland.

Habitat
Chalk and limestone areas, dry coastal localities, and heathland.

Life cycle
One generation a year. Overwinters as a pupa.

Larval foodplants
Bedstraws (*Galium* spp.). Recorded on purple loosestrife (*Lythrum salicaria*) and willowherbs (*Epilobium* spp.).

Imago
The wings are patterned in olive-ochreous and pinkish-red. On the hindwings there is a blackish-grey basal area. The head, thorax and abdomen are rose pink, faintly variegated with olive-ochreous. The antennae are thickened and hooked at the tip – they are smooth in the female and serrate in the male.

Variation can occur occasionally in the shade of ground colour, particularly on the forewings.

The moth flies at night, becoming active at dusk. It visits flowers, and is attracted to light.

Egg
The eggs are roundish in shape, and smooth in appearance, although the surface shows faint reticulations under high magnification. They are green in colour, and are laid singly on the under-

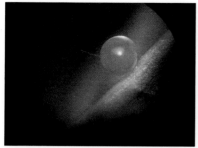

Egg; length 1·5 mm

Larva before 4th moult; length 32 mm

Larva after 4th moult; length 38 mm

Fully-grown larva; length 50 mm

Pupa; length 38 mm

side of a leaf of the foodplant, usually close to the midrib. They hatch in about seven days.

Larva
When newly hatched the larva is 3·5 mm long; the head is yellowish-green and the body pale greyish-green, lighter on the sides. On the twelfth segment is a small raised point. The larva gradually develops 'eye spots' on the front abdominal segments, but remains green until after the fourth moult, when the ground colour becomes brown. When it is fully grown its ground colour is usually greyish-brown marked with black; on two of the front abdominal segments are lilac, brown-centred 'eye spots', and there is a raised point on the twelfth segment. Another form of the larva is similarly marked, but its ground colour is green.

The eggshell is partially eaten. The larva feeds at night on both leaves and flowers of the food-plants, and if disturbed inflates the front portion of the body so that the 'eye spots' become much more prominent.

Pupa
The pupa is light brown marked with darker brown, dull in appearance, and rather rough in texture. There are small dark brown hooks on the abdominal segments. The pupa is enclosed in a very open-work cocoon in the litter on the surface of the ground, or just below the surface. Shortly before the adult emerges, the pupa uses its abdominal hooks to work its way partially out of the cocoon.

NOTODONTIDAE **Buff-tip**

Wingspan 55–68 mm

IMAGO
EGG
LARVA
PUPA

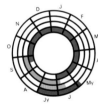

Distribution
Throughout the British Isles, although less common in Scotland and Ireland.

Habitat
Woodland, commons, parks, and gardens.

Life cycle
One generation a year. Over-winters as a pupa.

Larval foodplants
A variety of trees and shrubs including oak (*Quercus* spp.), birch (*Betula* spp.), sallow (*Salix* spp.), hazel (*Corylus avellana*), lime (*Tilia* spp.), and flowering cherries (*Prunus* spp.).

Imago
The forewings are silvery-grey, crossed by a few dark lines and with a yellow apical patch shaded with buff. The hindwings are pale yellow shaded with grey at the base. The abdomen is yellow and the thorax yellow and brown. The sexes are similar, but the antennae of the male are serrate and those of the female almost smooth.

Variation can occur in the amount of dark clouding in the yellow apical patch, and the level of grey basal shading on the hindwings.

The moth flies at night and is attracted to light. During the day it rests with the wings tight against the body, and the birch-bark colouring of the forewings together with the apical patch and yellow thorax give it an uncanny resemblance to a piece of broken twig.

Egg
The eggs are hemispherical, smooth, and white

Eggs on oak; width of egg 1 mm

Larva after 3rd moult; length 15 mm

Pupa; length 24 mm

Fully-grown larva; length 55 mm

with a black central spot. They are laid in neat batches on the undersides of leaves of the food-plants, and hatch in eight to ten days.

Larva
When newly hatched the larva is 3 mm long, and has an ochreous-brown body with black spots and soft hairs. The head, prothoracic collar and last segment are black. Through successive moults the ground colour becomes yellower, and the number of black markings increases. The body of the fully-grown larva is yellow with longitudinal broken black lines and transverse reddish-brown bands.

The head and spiracles are black, and the whole body bears fine soft white hairs.

The eggshell is not eaten. The larvae are gregarious until the final instar, when they become solitary. Particularly when young, they rest with the anal claspers elevated, and if alarmed throw up their heads in unison. Large groups of these larvae can defoliate branches.

Pupa
The pupa is dark purplish-brown, darker on the wingcases, slightly shiny, and rough in texture. It is found just below the surface of the ground.

NOTODONTIDAE **Puss Moth**

Wingspan 62–80 mm

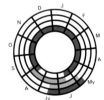

IMAGO
EGG
LARVA
PUPA

Distribution
Throughout the British Isles.

Habitat
Open woodland and hedgerows.

Life cycle
One generation a year. Over-winters as a pupa.

Larval foodplants
Sallows (*Salix* spp.), poplars (*Populus* spp.), and aspen (*P. tremula*).

Imago
The forewings are greyish-white, marked with wavy dark grey lines and black dots, and with yellowish veins. The thorax is grey with black spots, and the abdomen grey with darker grey transverse bands. The hindwings are white in the male, and greyish in the female – her forewings are also darker and more heavily marked than those of the male. The male's antennae are more strongly pectinate than those of the female.

Variation is uncommon, but some specimens from northern districts may be darker than those from the south.

The moth flies at night, and is attracted to light. During the day it may sometimes be found resting on tree trunks or fences.

Egg
The eggs are hemispherical, reddish-brown, and shiny, with a finely pitted surface. The micropyle is black, and sunk in a yellowish depression on the top of the egg. Eggs are laid singly or in groups of two or three on a leaf, usually on the upper surface, and hatch in twelve to fourteen days.

Cerura vinula (LINNAEUS)

Eggs; width 1·5 mm

Larva before 3rd moult; length 28 mm

Larva after 3rd moult; length 38 mm

Fully-grown larva; length 60 mm

Cocoon; length 40 mm

Pupa; length 28 mm

Larva

When newly hatched the larva is 4 mm long with 3 mm tail filaments; the head and body are black; the filaments and a pair of protuberances behind the head are deep red. Over the next two instars the sides become more yellow. Then a dark brown 'saddle' develops, and the sides become yellowish-green. In the fully-grown larva, the head is brown edged with red. There is a prominent hump on the metathorax, and a white-edged purplish-brown dorsal saddle. The sides are green, the spiracles white edged with black, and the anal claspers modified to form a pair of long tails. When annoyed, two red whip-like filaments are extruded from these tails and waved about; the head is then raised and the front segments hunched, presenting a very threatening display. If further irritated, an acid secretion is produced from the mouth.

The eggshell is not eaten. The larva usually rests on the upper surface of a leaf of the foodplant, with its head retracted into the first segment. When ready for pupation the body of the larva becomes purple.

Pupa

The pupa is dark blackish-brown, dull, and rough textured. It is contained in an extremely tough cocoon made of silk and chewed bark or wood, and situated on the trunk of the foodplant or on some similar object near by. When about to hatch, the pupa breaks the end of the cocoon, the pupal case splits and the moth emits an acid secretion which softens the ruptured area of the cocoon and allows the moth to emerge.

Breeding

A small log should be provided as a site for pupation – however, it is likely that the larva will chew up some part of the breeding cage for the purpose.

NOTODONTIDAE **Lobster Moth**

Wingspan 55–70 mm

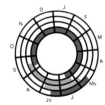

IMAGO
EGG
LARVA
PUPA

Distribution
England and Wales, south of a line between North Wales and the Wash, and the south-west of Ireland.

Habitat
Woodland.

Life cycle
One generation a year. Overwinters as a pupa.

Larval foodplants
Various trees and shrubs, particularly beech (*Fagus sylvatica*), oak (*Quercus* spp.), and birch (*Betula* spp.).

Imago
There are two distinct colour forms. In the first, the ground colour is brownish-grey; the forewings are marked with cream and brown and the hindwings with white costal marks. In the second form the ground colour is dark brown. The antennae of the male are strongly pectinate; those of the female are simple.

Variation can occur in both colour forms in the shade and markings of the wings.

The moth flies at night and is attracted to light, the females less readily than the males. When at rest on a tree trunk, the 'dead leaves' appearance of its wings provides excellent camouflage.

Egg
The eggs are hemispherical and smooth, with a pearly lustre. When laid the colour is creamy-white with a brown central spot. After about a week the shell becomes pale purple. The eggs are laid singly or in pairs on leaves of the foodplant, usually on the underside, and hatch in about ten days.

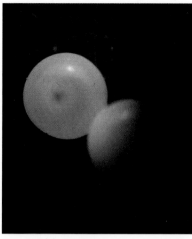
Egg; width 1·5 mm

2nd instar larva; length 7·5 mm

3rd instar larva; length 11 mm

4th & 5th instar larvae; length 15 mm, 24 mm

Fully-grown larva; length 70 mm

Pupa; length 23 mm

Larva

When newly hatched the larva is 5 mm long; it has very long thoracic legs and its body is banded with reddish-brown and dark brown. After the first moult a series of dorsal humps is present. When fully grown these humps are very prominent. The body becomes ochreous-brown in colour, and the head brown with darker brown stripes. The anal segment is greatly enlarged and bears two slender filaments in place of the anal prolegs. The thoracic legs are still very long.

Most of the eggshell is eaten. The larva then rests for about two days before beginning to nibble leaves. In the first two instars it bears a remarkable resemblance to an ant. When larger, it rests with the fore- and rear parts of its body raised, giving the 'Lobster' appearance which provided the species with its English name. It feeds at night. When disturbed, its long thoracic legs are extended and vibrated, giving the appearance of an agitated spider.

Pupa

The pupa is dark reddish-brown, smooth, and very shiny. It is enclosed in a papery cocoon among fallen leaves and litter on the surface of the ground.

NOTODONTIDAE **Iron Prominent**

Wingspan 42–50 mm

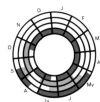

IMAGO
EGG
LARVA
PUPA

Distribution
Throughout the British Isles, except in Orkney and Shetland.

Habitat
Woodland.

Life cycle
Two generations a year except in the north, where there is only one, producing adult moths in June and July. Overwinters as a pupa.

Larval foodplants
Birch (*Betula* spp.). Also recorded on hazel (*Corylus avellana*) and alder (*Alnus glutinosa*).

Imago
The forewings are purplish-brown, marked with cream, ochreous, and rusty-red, and with a prominent scale tuft in the middle of the inner margin. The hindwings are brownish-grey. The sexes are similar, but the antennae of the male are shortly pectinate and those of the female are dentate.

Variation can occur in the ground colour, and specimens from northern districts are usually very dark in colour.

The moth flies at night and is attracted to light. During the day it may sometimes be found resting on tree trunks or fence posts.

Egg
The eggs are hemispherical and appear smooth, but under strong magnification the shell can be seen to be finely pitted. They are duck-egg blue in colour with a darker central spot. They are laid singly on the underside of leaves of the foodplant, and hatch in seven to ten days.

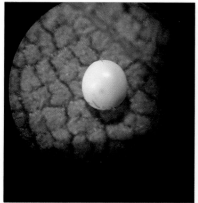

Egg; width 1 mm

Larva in July; length 16 mm

Fully-grown larva; length 30 mm

Fully-grown larva

Pupa; length 18 mm

Larva

When newly hatched, the larva is 2 mm long. During the early instars the larva is usually brown, but when fully grown its colour is very variable. The body may be yellowish-brown, or yellowish-green mottled with darker green and brown on the ventral surface. The head is pinkish-brown with darker speckling, and there are white-tipped dorsal humps on the first four abdominal segments, and another hump, not usually white-tipped, on the ninth segment.

The eggshell is not eaten. The larva feeds mainly at night, and usually rests on the underside of a leaf of the foodplant with its rear segments raised.

Pupa

The pupa is blackish-brown, blunt-ended, smooth, and very shiny. It is enclosed in a thin but tough papery cocoon of shiny white silk formed just beneath the surface of the ground.

NOTODONTIDAE **Great Prominent**

Wingspan 52–70 mm

IMAGO
EGG
LARVA
PUPA

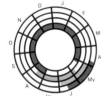

Distribution
The southern part of England; Wales and the Lake District. Local in Scotland as far as the west of Perthshire.

Habitat
Woodland with oaks.

Life cycle
One generation a year. Over-winters as a pupa.

Larval foodplants
Oak (*Quercus* spp.).

Imago
The forewings are greyish-brown, marked with darker grey, reddish-brown and ochreous, and there is a prominent scale tuft in the middle of the inner margin. The hindwings are yellowish-white marked with grey. The sexes are similar, except that the female tends to be slightly larger; her antennae are ciliate, while those of the male are pectinate.

Variation occurs in the ground colour of the forewings. Melanic specimens (f. *fusca*) sometimes occur.

The moth flies at night, and – the male especially – is attracted to light. During the day it can sometimes be found resting quite low down on tree trunks, or on wooden fence posts.

Egg
The eggs are hemispherical, pale duck-egg blue with a darker central spot. Under high magnification the shell appears finely pitted. They are laid in small batches on oak leaves, usually on the underside, and hatch in about ten days.

Eggs; width 1 mm

2nd instar larva; length 8 mm

Fully-grown larva; length 50 mm

Pupa; length 24 mm

Larva

When newly hatched, the larva is 3 mm long, with the head yellow-green and the body green with raised black dots each bearing a fine hair. After the second moult there are oblique red and yellow streaks along the sides. In the fully-grown larva, the head is yellowish-green with pale yellow lines, and a broader reddish line low down on each side. The body is green spotted with yellow. On either side of the thoracic segments is a red and yellow line, and on each side of the abdominal segments there are oblique red and yellow streaks.

The eggshell is not eaten. During the first two instars the larvae 'filigree' the leaves, and if disturbed drop off and hang by a silken thread. By the time they are half grown, they eat the tips of the leaves, leaving the midrib, but during the last instar the whole substance of the leaf is eaten. When resting the head and front segments are held thrown back.

Pupa

The pupa is blackish-brown, smooth and very shiny. It is enclosed in a tough cocoon beneath the surface of the ground.

LYMANTRIIDAE **The Vapourer**

♂ wingspan 35–38 mm

♀ body length 18 mm

IMAGO
EGG
LARVA
PUPA

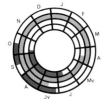

Distribution
Throughout the British Isles.

Habitat
Woodlands, parks, gardens, hedgerows, and bushy places.

Life cycle
One generation a year, with a partial second generation except in the north. Overwinters as an egg.

Larval foodplants
Most deciduous trees and shrubs. In Scotland, reported to favour birch (*Betula* spp.).

Imago
The forewings of the male are rich reddish-brown with darker brown shading and a conspicuous kidney-shaped white spot in the tornal angle. The hindwings are also rich reddish-brown and the antennae are strongly pectinate. The female is virtually wingless; her body is pale grey and furry, and her antennae are very weakly pectinate.

Variation can occur in the depth of colour of the male's wings.

The male flies by day, and may be seen flying jerkily and swiftly in sunshine in search of a female, who usually remains on her cocoon, although very occasionally she may sit close to it.

Egg
The eggs are pale brownish-white with a flattened top. In the centre is a brown spot surrounded by a white ring; this in turn is encompassed by a brown ring. The eggs are laid in one batch, almost always on the cocoon. Having overwintered the eggs of any particular batch hatch a few at a time over a period of two or three weeks, commencing in late April.

Orgyia antiqua (LINNAEUS)

Eggs on cocoon

Eggs; width 1 mm

Newly-hatched larva; length 2 mm

Fully-grown larva; length 30 mm

Cocoon

Pupae; length ♂ 12 mm, ♀ 20 mm

Larva

When newly hatched the larva's head is black, and its body dark brown and covered with tubercles bearing long fine hairs. There is a whitish dorsal patch on the ninth segment. After the third moult the larva develops its characteristic hair tufts. When it is fully grown its body is grey, marked with black patches and raised red spots bearing tufts of light ochreous hairs. There are four 'shaving brush' tufts of yellow hairs on the back, a forward-pointing tuft of longer dark grey hairs on each side of the head, and a single long backward-pointing tuft of brown hairs on the eighth segment. Female larvae are much larger than males.

The eggshells are eaten. The larva usually rests quite exposed on the leaves of the foodplants – it is often a common sight in suburban parks and tree-lined streets.

Pupa

The pupa is black, very shiny, and all parts except the wingcases of the male are covered with fine whitish hairs. The female pupa is much larger and plumper than the male, and has no wingcases. The pupa is fastened by its cremaster to the inside layer of the double cocoon, which consists of whitish-yellow silk mixed with larval hairs. It may be situated under a leaf of the foodplant, in a bark crevice, on a fence, under a windowsill or eaves, or on a gatepost. The adult moth emerges in two to three weeks.

LYMANTRIIDAE **Pale Tussock**

♂ wingspan ♂ 46–52 mm, ♀ 58–70 mm

IMAGO
EGG
LARVA
PUPA

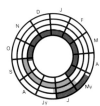

Distribution
Throughout England and Wales, and southern Ireland.

Habitat
Woodland, hedgerows.

Life cycle
One generation a year. Over-winters as a pupa.

Larval foodplants
A wide variety of trees including oak (*Quercus* spp.), birch (*Betula* spp.), lime (*Tilia* spp.), hazel (*Corylus avellana*), and hop (*Humulus lupulus*).

Imago
The ground colour of the wings of the male is pale grey; the forewings are shaded and lined with brownish-grey. The female is larger than the male, with wings similarly marked but whitish-grey. Her antennae are weakly pectinate, while those of the male are much more strongly pectinate.

Variation can occur in the depth of ground colour of the wings, and melanic specimens are sometimes found.

The moth flies at night and is attracted to light. When at rest the hairy forelegs are extended in front of the head.

Egg
The eggs are rounded with a depression on the top, and are greyish-white with a grey spot in the depression. They are laid in batches on the leaves of the foodplants, usually on the underside, and hatch in twelve to fourteen days.

Calliteara pudibunda (LINNAEUS)

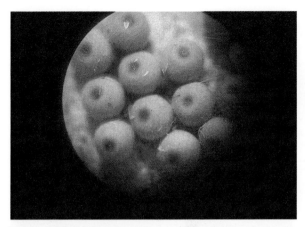

Eggs; width 1·25 mm

Larvae – three colour forms

Fully-grown larva; length 30 mm

Pupa; length 18 mm

Larva

When newly hatched the larva is 2·5 mm long and ochreous brown in colour, with black transverse dorsal bands and long black hairs. The colouring of the older larva is very variable – when it is fully grown its body may be green or yellowish-green. There is a 'shaving brush' on the back of each of the first four abdominal segments. These hair tufts may be yellow, white, or dark grey. Between the tufts there are black transverse bands. On the eighth segment is a thin backward-pointing pencil of hairs which may be rose pink or blackish-grey. The body is covered with long hairs, which may be either grey or pinkish.

The eggshells are eaten. During the first instar the larva hangs on a silken thread, and its long hairs make it resemble a tiny spider. If alarmed, it drops to the ground on its thread. It feeds by day or night.

Pupa

The pupa is light reddish-brown on the abdomen, darker brown on the thorax and wingcases, very shiny, and covered with fine hairs. It is attached by tail hooks to the inside of a cocoon of whitish silk mixed with larval hairs, spun among leaves, or in litter on the ground.

LYMANTRIIDAE **Brown-tail**

Wingspan 36–43 mm

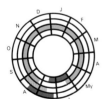

Distribution
Southern and eastern England.

Habitat
Hedgerows, woodland, and bushy places.

Life cycle
One generation a year. Over-winters as a young larva.

Larval foodplants
A variety of trees and shrubs, including oak (*Quercus* spp.), hawthorn (*Crataegus monogyna*), blackthorn (*Prunus spinosa*), and sallow (*Salix* spp.).

Imago
The wings, thorax, and part of the abdomen nearest to the thorax are white. In the male, the abdomen is brown on the dorsal surface with a dark brown anal tuft. In the female it is grey on the dorsal surface, and the brown anal tuft is much larger. Females are larger than males, and their antennae are much less strongly pectinate.

Variation is uncommon – occasionally there may be a few small black dots on the forewing.

The moth flies at night, is attracted to light, and during the day may sometimes be disturbed from foliage.

Egg
The eggs are round and slightly flattened on the upper surface, smooth, shiny, and orange in

Egg batch; length 15 mm

Eggs; width 0·5 mm

Hibernaculum; length 70 mm

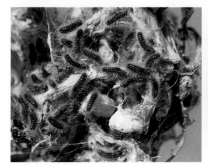

Larvae in April; length 11 mm

Fully-grown larvae; length 30 mm

Pupa; length 17 mm

colour. They are laid in batches on the twigs or leaves of the foodplants, and are completely covered with dark brown hairs from the anal tuft of the female. They hatch in about three weeks.

Larva

When newly hatched the larva is 2 mm long, the head is black and the body yellowish-ochreous with two dark brown transverse bands and ochreous hairs. When the larva is fully grown, the body is dark grey with long golden hairs; there is a broken lateral line of white spots and two prominent red dorsal spots on the sixth and seventh abdominal segments.

The eggshell is eaten. After hatching, the larvae live gregariously in a silken web until late summer. When about 5 mm long, they weave a hibernaculum of very tough silk in which to spend the winter, and they commence feeding again at the beginning of April. When fully grown they dispense with the web and feed by day or night.

Pupa

The pupa is dark blackish-brown and dull, and all parts except the wingcases and antennae are hairy. It is enclosed in a cocoon of brownish silk mixed with larval hairs and spun among the leaves of the foodplant. The adult moth emerges in about three weeks.

Caution

The hairs of the anal tuft of the moth, and those of the larva, are extremely irritating to the skin, and can cause severe rashes. Every stage of this moth should be treated with great respect, since the eggs are covered with hairs from the anal tuft, and larval hairs are worked into the cocoon.

LYMANTRIIDAE **Black Arches**

♂ wingspan 42–46 mm

♀ wingspan 50–58 mm

IMAGO
EGG
LARVA
PUPA

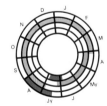

Distribution
England and Wales south of a line between North Wales and the Wash.

Habitat
Woodland.

Life cycle
One generation a year. Over-winters as an egg.

Larval foodplants
Oak (*Quercus* spp.). Has been recorded on birch (*Betula* spp.), aspen (*Populus tremula*), and other trees. In Europe can be a pest on Scots pine (*Pinus sylvestris*) and Norway spruce (*Picea abies*).

Imago
The forewings are white with black zig-zag transverse lines and black spots. The hindwings are greyish-brown, darker near the margins. The wing fringes are chequered black and white. The thorax is white with black spots and the abdomen rose pink with black marks. The antennae of the male are strongly pectinate, and those of the female very weakly so. The male's legs are chequered black and white, and the female's are mainly black. Females are larger than males, and have an ovipositor.

Variation occurs frequently in the number of black markings on the forewings. Wholly melanic specimens (f. *eremita*) sometimes occur.

The moth flies at night. Males are readily attracted to light, but females very seldom. They may sometimes be found resting on tree trunks during the day.

Eggs; width 1 mm

Eggs showing larvae within

Newly-hatched larva; length 2 mm

Larva in May; length 11 mm

Fully-grown larva; length 36 mm

Pupa; length 20 mm

Egg

The eggs are roundish-oval and pale brown, with a slightly pitted surface. They are laid singly, or in twos or threes, in crevices in the bark. By the end of September the larva is fully formed within the egg, and is visible through the shell, although it does not emerge until the following April.

Larva

When newly hatched the larva's head is black, and its body brown and white with black hairs. When it is fully grown its head is greyish-brown marked with darker brown, and its body is grey with a wide blackish dorsal stripe interrupted by whitish patches. The body bears raised tubercles, both red and whitish, all of which bear tufts of whitish hairs, and there are two forward-pointing 'pencils' of black hair behind the head.

The eggshell is partly eaten. During the first instar the larvae hang on silken threads, and when disturbed are very active. In later instars they rest in bark crevices during the day, emerging at night to feed.

Pupa

The pupa is blackish-brown, very shiny, and covered with tufts of short hairs. The hairs on the thorax are black, and those on the rest of the body are pink. The pupa is contained in a flimsy, rather transparent cocoon, usually situated in a bark crevice, and the adult moth emerges in about two weeks.

ARCTIIDAE (LITHOSIINAE) **Muslin Footman**

Wingspan 19–23 mm

IMAGO ▪
EGG ▪
LARVA ▪
PUPA ▪

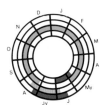

Distribution
Throughout the British Isles as far north as the Scottish Highlands.

Habitat
Stony, rocky places, and the vicinity of old stone walls, especially dry-stone walls.

Life cycle
One generation a year. Overwinters as a young larva.

Larval foodplants
Lichens growing on rocks and stone walls, especially the orange *Xanthoria parietina* and the yellow *Caloplaca citrina*.

Imago
The wings are semi-transparent and flimsy in texture, and have a somewhat pearly lustre. The forewings are light brownish-grey with two zigzag transverse brown lines with a brown discal spot between. The hindwings are ochreous. The sexes are similarly marked, but the female is usually the smaller, and her antennae are simple, while those of the male are finely ciliate.

Variation can occur in the intensity of the brown markings on the forewings, and the amount of brownish clouding near the outer margins.

The moth becomes active at dusk. Females are much more sedentary than males, and seem to fly very little. During the day both sexes rest concealed under or among stones and rocks.

Eggs; width 0·6 mm | Fully-grown larva; length 12 mm | Pupae; length 8 mm

Egg

The eggs are roundish-oval in shape, finely reticulated and glistening. When laid they are creamy-white, but just before hatching they turn ochreous with a brown spot on the top. They are laid in small batches on the underside of loose stones such as those capping a dry-stone wall, or in sheltered spots on rocks, and they hatch in about twelve to fourteen days.

Larva

When newly hatched the larva is 2 mm long, with a brown head and an ochreous body with long whitish hairs. From the first moult until it is fully grown, the head is brown and the body greyish-brown with greyish-brown hairs. There is a brown dorsal line bordered on either side by a broad yellow stripe. The subdorsal line is dark brown, and the fourth abdominal segment bears a black dorsal spot.

The eggshell is eaten. The young larva feeds until the autumn, usually October, when it goes into hibernation on a pad of silk beneath a stone or in a rock crevice. It recommences feeding in spring – it feeds at night except during the final instar, when it will often feed in sunshine. During April and early May it may be found by turning over the capping stones of dry-stone walls; when at rest it conceals itself under these stones, or in crevices in rocks. If disturbed, the larva rolls into a ring.

Pupa

The pupa is yellowish-green, shiny, and rather translucent. There are subdorsal lines of dark brown spots, and when the pupa is newly formed there is a yellowish dorsal spot corresponding to the black dorsal spot of the larva. This fades as the pupa matures. The wingcases and ventral surface are smooth and pale green. The pupa is attached by tail hooks to the inside of a flimsy transparent cocoon of greyish silk mixed with larval hairs. Small groups of cocoons may be found beneath stones or in crevices. The eyes of the pupa become black after about ten days, and during the following week the whole pupa becomes brownish. The adult moth emerges after two and a half to three weeks.

Breeding

Overwintering the larvae can be a problem, as the amount of humidity required is critical – if not correct, the larva will either dry up or go mouldy. I find the best method is to keep a stone bearing the foodplant lichens in a plastic box outdoors in a sheltered, shaded position. The larvae remain under the stone during the day and the coldest months, but can emerge to feed at night when the weather is suitable. A light spraying of rain-water on the inside of the lid, to maintain a few drops there, together with an occasional light spraying on the lichens, is usually sufficient to provide the correct level of humidity.

ARCTIIDAE (LITHOSIINAE) **Common Footman**

Wingspan 30–38 mm

IMAGO
EGG
LARVA
PUPA

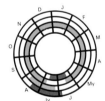

Distribution
England, Wales, and Ireland, and also local populations in southern and eastern Scotland.

Habitat
Woodland, bushy places, and hedgerows.

Life cycle
One generation a year. Over-winters as a young larva.

Larval foodplants
Lichens growing on trees, bushes and fences. In captivity, mature larvae will eat the foliage of some trees and shrubs, including sallow (*Salix* spp.).

Imago
The forewings are leaden-grey with a slender orange-yellow streak along the costa, narrowing to a point before it reaches the apex. The hind-wings are broad, and pale ochreous-yellow. The head and anal tuft are yellow, and the thorax and abdomen grey. The sexes are similar, but the antennae of the male are weakly ciliate while those of the female are simple.

This species may be confused with the Scarce Footman (*E. complana*). The differences are that in the Scarce Footman the costal streak continues right to the apex without narrowing, and the Scarce Footman when resting keeps its wings rolled tightly round its body, while the Common Footman's wings are folded flat over its back.

Variation can occur occasionally in the shade of ground colour of the wings.

The moth flies at night, becoming active at dusk.

Egg; width 0·8 mm   Fully-grown larva; length 19 mm   Pupa; length 11 mm

It visits flowers and will come to light. If disturbed during the day it falls to the ground and remains motionless, 'playing dead'.

Egg

The eggs are hemispherical, shining, and white, with a finely pitted surface. They are laid either singly or in small batches on bark, and hatch in about ten days.

Larva

When newly hatched, the larva is 1·5 mm in length. The head is brown and the body ochreous with long fine greyish hairs. After the first moult and until the larva is fully grown, the head is black and the body dark grey with black dorsal and subdorsal lines; there is an orange spiracular stripe along the abdominal segments, and the hairs below this stripe are yellow, while those on the rest of the body are black.

The eggshell is eaten. The larva feeds for a few weeks before hibernation, and recommences feeding in early spring. It feeds at night, but during the last instar may also feed in sunshine.

Pupa

The pupa is reddish-brown with rows of blackish dorsal and subdorsal marks. The segmental divisions are black. The surface is smooth and very shiny, and the larval skin remains attached to the cremaster. The pupa is contained in a rather transparent cocoon of whitish silk spun in a crevice, and the adult moth emerges after three to four weeks.

ARCTIIDAE (ARCTIINAE) **Garden Tiger**

Wingspan 50–78 mm

IMAGO   ■
EGG
LARVA
PUPA   ■

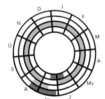

Distribution
Throughout the British Isles.

Habitat
Woodland, gardens, roadside verges and waste ground.

Life cycle
One generation a year. Over-winters as a young larva.

Larval foodplants
Polyphagous. A tremendous variety of low-growing plants is eaten; special favourites are dock (*Rumex* spp.), dead-nettle (*Lamium* spp.), dandelion (*Taraxacum* spp.), and nasturtiums (*Tropaeolum*).

Imago
The forewings are dark brown with a network of creamy-white streaks, and the hindwings are orange-red with blue-black spots. The thorax is dark brown, with the patagia marked with red; the abdomen is orange-red with black transverse dorsal bands. The sexes are similarly marked, but females are usually larger, and their antennae are ciliate, while those of the males are pectinate. The shafts of the antennae are white.

Variation occurs very frequently, in both the pattern and extent of the forewing markings, and in the ground colour and pattern of spots on the hindwing. Extreme aberrations can be obtained in captivity by selective breeding from wild variations.

Although seen very occasionally during the day, the moth flies at night and is attracted to light.

Egg
The eggs are hemispherical and shiny, with a finely pitted surface. When laid the shell colour is pale greenish-white, becoming yellowish-green

'Fright' reaction

Eggs; width 1 mm

5th instar larva; length 25 mm

Fully-grown larva; length 45 mm

Pupa; length 30 mm

and finally brown. The eggs are laid in large batches on the undersides of leaves of the food-plants and hatch in about ten days.

Larva

When newly hatched the larva is 3 mm long; the head is black and the body yellowish-ochreous with black spots and long dark hairs. After the first moult the body is brown and much more hairy. When the larva is fully grown the head is black and the body dark brown with small white dots in the spiracular region. The whole body is now densely covered with fine hairs – those on the back are long, black at the base, becoming white about halfway along their length; the hairs on the thoracic segments and along the sides below the spiracles are shorter and reddish-brown.

The eggshells are eaten. The young larva feeds for about a month and then hibernates among dead leaves or other surface litter, recommencing feeding in early April. The moulted skins are partially eaten. The long hairs of the fully grown larva have given it the popular name of 'Woolly Bear'. In former years it was a common sight in gardens and in the countryside, as it marched briskly about; nowadays it is less often seen.

Pupa

The pupa is blackish-brown and shiny, and is enclosed in a loose cocoon of silk mixed with larval hairs, situated on the ground among dead leaves or in litter. The adult emerges in two to three weeks.

ARCTIIDAE (ARCTIINAE) **Clouded Buff**

♂ wingspan 44–50 mm

♀ wingspan 35–42 mm

IMAGO
EGG
LARVA
PUPA

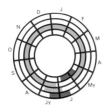

Distribution
Throughout the British Isles, except Orkney, Shetland and the Isle of Man.

Habitat
Heathland, moorland, chalk downland, and open areas in woodland.

Life cycle
One generation a year. Overwinters as a young larva.

Larval foodplants
A wide variety of low-growing plants, including heather (*Calluna vulgaris*), heaths (*Erica* spp.), dandelion (*Taraxacum* spp.), plantains (*Plantago* spp.), docks (*Rumex* spp.), lucerne (*Medicago sativa*), and annual meadow-grass (*Poa annua*).

Imago
Sexually dimorphic. In the male, the forewings are yellow, edged with rose pink. There is a grey-brown discal spot edged with pink. The hindwings are white, edged with rose pink; there is a grey submarginal band and a grey-brown discal mark. The antennae are pectinate, the head and thorax yellow, and the abdomen white with grey dorsal spots. In the female, the forewings are orange with brownish-red veins and discal mark; the hindwings are orange, submarginally and basally marked with dark grey; the antennae are dentate, the head and thorax orange, and the abdomen orange with black dorsal bands. Males are larger than females.

Variation consists mainly of either an increase or decrease in the amount of grey shading and marking on the hindwings.

Eggs on bell heather

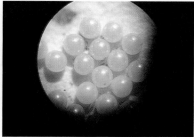

Eggs; width 1 mm

Larva before hibernation; length 9 mm

Larva in April; length 25 mm

Fully-grown larva; length 35 mm

Pupa; length 16 mm

Males are easily disturbed from low vegetation during the day, and sometimes fly freely in sunshine. Females are less readily put to flight, and then only fly for a very short distance before dropping into the undergrowth. Both sexes fly at night – the males are readily attracted to light, but the extremely sluggish females very seldom.

Egg
The eggs are hemispherical, shiny, very finely pitted, and creamy-white in colour. They are laid in small neat batches on the leaves or flowers of the foodplants. The eggs in any one batch hatch in sequence, two or three each day, beginning about ten days after being laid.

Larva
When newly hatched, the larva is 2 mm long; the head is brown and the body ochreous with whitish hairs. After the first moult and until hibernation the body is grey with black spots, a yellow dorsal stripe and ochreous hairs. After hibernation the body and hairs are dark brown, and the dorsal stripe is red and white. When the larva is fully grown the body is brown with black tubercles bearing tufts of brown hairs, and with a reddish-yellow dorsal stripe.

The eggshell is partially eaten. The young larva feeds for about six weeks and then hibernates completely until the following March or beginning of April, when feeding recommences. It feeds at night, and if disturbed drops from the foodplant and will run extremely fast.

Pupa
The pupa is generally blackish-brown, but reddish-brown between the abdominal segments. It is shiny with a roughened surface, and the larval skin remains attached to the cremaster. The pupa is enclosed in a thin, transparent cocoon of white silk spun on the surface of the ground among leaves or in litter, and the adult moth emerges in about three weeks.

Breeding
It is extremely difficult to overwinter Clouded Buff larvae successfully in captivity. Best results may be obtained by keeping the young larvae warm, thereby ensuring that they are about half grown before they go into hibernation.

ARCTIIDAE (ARCTIINAE) **Buff Ermine**

♂ wingspan 34–42 mm

♀ wingspan 34–42 mm

IMAGO
EGG
LARVA
PUPA

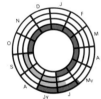

Distribution
Throughout the British Isles.

Habitat
Woodland, waste ground, gardens, and hedgerows.

Life cycle
One generation a year. Over-winters as a pupa.

Larval foodplants
A wide variety of low-growing plants, both wild and cultivated, including dandelion (*Taraxacum* spp.), dock (*Rumex* spp,), and plantains (*Plantago* spp.). Also recorded on birch (*Betula* spp.).

Imago
The wings are yellowish-buff. The forewings are marked with a few black spots, and the hindwings with a greyish spot near the dorsum and occasionally a few other grey spots. The head and body are yellowish-buff, the abdomen bearing black spots. The ground colour of the female is paler than that of the male, and her antennae are dentate, while those of the male are shortly pectinate.

Variation is common, and consists of differences in the amount and extent of the black on the wing – it may be almost absent or practically fill the wing area (ab. *zatima*).

The moth flies at night and is attracted to light.

Egg
The eggs are hemispherical, smooth, shiny, and greenish-white in colour, becoming grey just before hatching. They are laid in large neat batches on the undersides of leaves of the foodplants, and hatch in seven to ten days.

Eggs; width 1 mm

Larva after 4th moult; length 28 mm

Fully-grown larva; length 32 mm

Pupa; length 15 mm

Larva

When newly hatched, the larva is 2·5 mm long; the head is light brown and the body whitish-ochreous with black hairs. After the first moult the body is more yellow. After the third moult it is grey-green with dark olive-green subdorsal stripes and whitish hairs. After the next moult the body is greyer and the subdorsal stripes are edged below with white. There is a mixture of black and grey hairs. When the larva is fully grown the head is light brown and the body brown with a reddish dorsal stripe, a yellowish spiracular stripe and a dense covering of brown hairs.

The eggshell is eaten. If disturbed, the larva falls to the ground and rolls in a ring. It is often found in gardens, where it normally rests underneath a leaf of the foodplant.

Pupa

The pupa is dark reddish-brown, smooth, and shiny. It is enclosed in a thin cocoon of silk mixed with larval hairs, which is usually situated among dead leaves and litter on the surface of the ground.

ARCTIIDAE (ARCTIINAE) **Scarlet Tiger**

Wingspan 52–58 mm

IMAGO
EGG
LARVA
PUPA

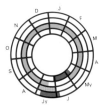

■ Distribution
East Kent, and the south and west of both England and Wales; populations are very local.

Habitat
River banks, water meadows, damp coastal areas, fens, and marshy ground.

Life cycle
One generation a year. Over-winters as a young larva.

Larval foodplants
A variety of herbaceous plants including common nettle (*Urtica dioica*), comfrey (*Symphytum* spp.), dock (*Rumex* spp.), and meadow-sweet (*Filipendula ulmaria*).

Imago
The forewings are greenish-black with a metallic sheen, and marked with large creamy spots, some of which are shaded with orange. The hindwings are scarlet with metallic blue-black blotches. The head is greenish-black, the thorax greenish-black with two orange streaks, and the abdomen scarlet with a black dorsal line and ventral surface. The sexes are similarly marked; the antennae of the male are setose-ciliate and those of the female simple.

Variation is frequent, and consists mainly of differences in the extent of the wing markings. In the striking variety ab. *rossica* the ground colour of the hindwings is yellow.

Although the moth flies in sunshine, and may also be put to flight from low herbage during the day, it is also active at night, and both sexes are attracted to light.

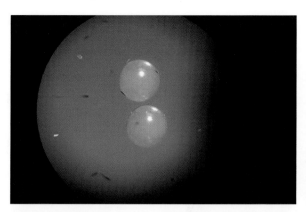

Eggs; width 1 mm

Larva before hibernation; length 14 mm

Fully-grown larva; length 25 mm

Pupa; length 19 mm

Egg
The eggs are hemispherical, smooth, and shiny. When laid, they are greenish-white in colour, becoming grey just before hatching. The eggs are scattered at random by the female and not attached to anything. They hatch in about seven days.

Larva
When newly hatched the larva is 2 mm long; the head is black and the body greyish with long fine hairs. When the larva is fully grown, the head is black and the body purplish-black with yellow and white dorsal and subdorsal stripes. The tubercles bear a mixture of black and grey hairs.

The eggshells are not eaten. The young larva feeds until about the beginning of September, and then hibernates on the surface of the ground among dead leaves or in litter, recommencing feeding in April. Until the final instar it feeds mainly at night, resting away from the foodplant among herbage on the ground during the day, but when fully grown it will often feed in sunshine. If disturbed, it falls to the ground and rolls into a ring.

Pupa
The pupa is blackish-brown on the dorsal surface, reddish-brown elsewhere, smooth and very shiny. It is enclosed in a very thin transparent cocoon spun on the surface of the ground among dead leaves or in litter. The adult moth emerges in about three weeks.

ARCTIIDAE (ARCTIINAE) **The Cinnabar**

Wingspan 35–45 mm

IMAGO
EGG
LARVA
PUPA

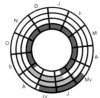

Distribution
Throughout the British Isles, but in Scotland it is local and confined mainly to coastal districts in the east and west.

Habitat
Waste ground, downland, grassland, heathland, and sand dunes where the foodplants grow.

Life cycle
One generation a year. Overwinters as a pupa.

Larval foodplants
Ragwort and groundsels (*Senecio* spp.).

Imago
The forewings are greyish-black with a scarlet subcostal streak, a shorter scarlet streak along the dorsum and two scarlet spots on the termen. The hindwings are scarlet with black fringes, and the head and body are black. The sexes are similar – both have setose-ciliate antennae – but females are usually smaller than males.

Variation occurs sometimes in the extent of the scarlet marking on the forewings. Extreme varieties can be produced in captivity – the wings may be all black or all red, or the scarlet may be replaced by yellow (ab. *flavescens*).

The moth flies at night and is readily attracted to light. During the day it may be disturbed very easily from low herbage.

Egg batch on ragwort

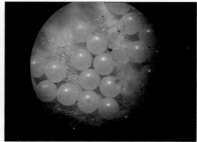

Eggs; width 0·8 mm

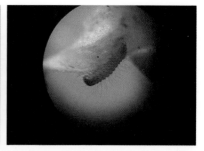

Newly-hatched larva; length 2 mm

Larvae on ragwort

Fully-grown larvae; length 23 mm

Pupa; length 13 mm

Egg

The eggs are hemispherical, smooth and shiny. Yellow when laid, they become grey just before hatching. They are laid in neat batches on the undersides of the lower leaves of the foodplants, and hatch in seven to ten days.

Larva

When newly hatched, the larva's head is brown and its body greyish-ochreous with long whitish hairs. After the first moult the body becomes banded, and this pattern remains throughout the larval stage. When the larva is fully grown the head is black; the body is banded alternately with black and orange-yellow, and bears a few short blackish hairs and some longer white ones.

The eggshells are not eaten. The larvae are gregarious and feed by day or night. Large numbers of them will completely strip patches of ragwort of leaves and flowers, leaving only the tough stalks.

Pupa

The pupa is very dark reddish-brown, shiny, and with a slightly pitted surface. It is enclosed in a thin, loose cocoon either just beneath the surface of the ground or in litter on the surface.

NOLIDAE **Short-cloaked Moth**

Wingspan 15–20 mm

IMAGO ■
EGG ▦
LARVA ▨
PUPA ■

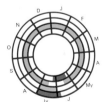

Distribution
Throughout England and Wales.

Habitat
Woodland, hedgerows, bushy places, and commons.

Life cycle
One generation a year. Over-winters as a young larva.

Larval foodplants
Hawthorn (*Crataegus monogyna*), blackthorn (*Prunus spinosa*), and sometimes cultivated fruit trees such as apple and plum.

Imago
The forewings are pale grey with a dark brownish-grey basal area bounded by a blackish line. There is brownish-grey shading towards the outer margin, and there are tufts of raised scales in the discal area. The hindwing is pale brownish-grey. The sexes are similar, except that the antennae of the male are pectinate whereas those of the female are simple.

Variations can occur in the shade of the ground colour and the amount and density of the dark shading on the forewings.

The moth flies at night, becoming active at dusk, and during the day rests on tree trunks or branches. The English name refers to the dark basal area of the forewings.

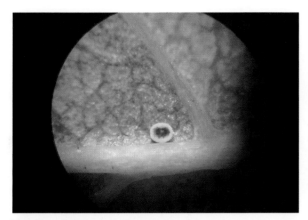

Egg; length 0·5 mm

Fully-grown larva; length 20 mm

Cocoon; length 10 mm

Pupa; length 7 mm

Egg

The eggs are oval in shape, finely ribbed, with a smooth area on the top. When laid they are creamy-white, with the smooth area slightly more yellow. After four to five days this area becomes purplish-brown. The eggs are laid singly on the underside of a leaf of the foodplant, usually near the midrib or a vein, and hatch after ten to fourteen days.

Larva

When newly hatched, the larva is 1 mm long; the head is black and the body ochreous with black dorsal marks and long dark hairs. When the larva is fully grown, the head is dark brown, and the body purplish-brown with a dark brown pro-thoracic plate; a white dorsal stripe is bordered by alternate white and purplish-brown patches, and reddish tubercles bear grey hairs of varying lengths. The larva has only four pairs of prolegs.

The eggshell is not eaten. After hatching, the larva feeds for a few weeks and then hibernates in a bark crevice, protected by a thin silken web, from about mid-August until the following April, when feeding recommences. It feeds mainly at night, and during the day rests either on a stem or on the underside of a leaf.

Pupa

The abdomen of the pupa is pale brown; the thorax and wingcases are a darker greenish-brown. The pupa is shiny, slightly rough in texture, and the larval skin remains attached to the cremaster. It is enclosed in a tough, opaque cocoon, which is truncated at the head end, tapered towards the tail end, and attached to a twig of the foodplant. The adult moth emerges in about two weeks.

NOCTUIDAE (NOCTUINAE) **Shuttle-shaped Dart**

♂ wingspan 30–32 mm

♀ wingspan 30–32 mm

IMAGO
EGG
LARVA
PUPA

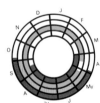

Distribution
ssp. *puta*: England and Wales as far north as Lancashire and Yorkshire. ssp. *insula*: Isles of Scilly.

Habitat
Woodland, both waste and cultivated ground, and marshy ground.

Life cycle
Two or three generations a year. Overwinters as a larva.

Larval foodplants
A variety of herbaceous plants including docks (*Rumex* spp.), dandelions (*Taraxacum* spp.), and knotgrass (*Polygonum* spp.).

Imago
The sexes differ markedly. The forewings of the male are light brown with a blackish-brown reniform stigma and basal patch. The hindwings are whitish with brown veins, and the antennae very shortly pectinate, tapering off to become simple at the tips. The forewings of the female are blackish with ochreous elongated orbicular stigmata and brown fringes. The hindwings are grey and the antennae simple. In ssp. *insula* the male's forewings are much more strongly marked than in ssp. *puta*.

Variation occurs in the shade of ground colour in the male's forewings.

The moth flies at night, visits flowers, and both sexes are attracted to light. The generations tend to overlap, and there is an extended emergence from each, so adult moths may be seen from April to October.

Eggs; width 0·8 mm   Fully-grown larva; length 30 mm   Pupa; length 14 mm

Egg

The eggs are rounded with a flattened base, shiny, and strongly ribbed. When laid they are creamy-white in colour, but within a couple of days a pattern of reddish-brown blotches develops. The eggs are laid in batches on the underside of leaves of the foodplant, and hatch in about seven days.

Larva

When newly hatched the larva is 1 mm long; the head is black and the body greyish-brown with short whitish hairs. When the larva is fully grown, the head is brown and shiny, marked with darker brown, the body is ochreous-brown with greyish mottling and dark brown wavy lines, and the spiracles are black.

The eggshell is partly eaten. The larva feeds only at night, and during the day rests hidden away from the foodplant. Overwintering larvae will feed during a spell of mild weather.

Pupa

The abdomen of the pupa is reddish-brown; the thorax and wingcases are much darker. The surface of the pupa is smooth and shiny, and the cremaster bears a pair of short divergent spines. The pupa is formed beneath the surface of the ground and the adult emerges in about two weeks.

Breeding

In captivity the larvae will eat slices of raw carrot.

NOCTUIDAE (NOCTUINAE) **Large Yellow Underwing**

♂ wingspan 50–60 mm

♀ wingspan 50–60 mm

IMAGO
EGG
LARVA
PUPA

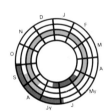

Distribution
Throughout the British Isles.

Habitat
Almost any type of habitat is suitable – woodland, downland, waste ground, heaths, moors, and gardens.

Life cycle
One generation a year. Overwinters as a larva.

Larval foodplants
The foliage, stems and roots of a wide variety of wild and garden herbaceous plants and grasses. Special favourites are dandelions (*Taraxacum* spp.), dock (*Rumex* spp.), chickweed (*Stellaria* spp.), and dead-nettle (*Lamium* spp.).

Imago
Sexually dimorphic. The ground colour of the forewing in the male is darker than that of the female, but in both sexes it is extremely variable. In the male it ranges from rich brown to blackish-brown, or it may be heavily mottled, sometimes with bluish-grey. The usual ground colour of the forewing in the female ranges from ochreous with darker brown freckling, through grey with darker grey freckling to reddish-ochreous. In both sexes the hindwings are orange-yellow with a black border and the antennae are setose.

This is an extremely variable species in the ground colour of the forewings, but occasionally additional slight variation occurs in the shade of yellow or the width of the black border of the hindwings.

The Large Yellow Underwing is extremely common – the numbers of residents are increased by arrivals of migrants. It flies at night, visits flowers, and is attracted to light, often in great numbers. There is a prolonged emergence period. After emerging, the moths feed for a week or two and

Noctua pronuba (LINNAEUS)

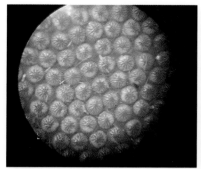  

Eggs; width 0·5 mm   Half-grown larva; length 18 mm   Fully-grown larva (brown form); length 40 mm

Fully-grown larva (green form); length 40 mm   Pupa; length 27 mm

then aestivate for about a month before egg-laying begins – so there is an apparent increase in the population during August, caused by these individuals becoming active again. During the day, the moth rests in undergrowth or low herbage, and if disturbed flies off swiftly and erratically, the sudden flash of colour from the hindwings being quite startling.

Egg
The eggs are globular with a flattened base, shiny and strongly ribbed. When laid they are pale yellow, but begin to darken after twenty-four hours, gradually becoming creamy-white and heavily patterned with purplish-brown mottling. They are laid in very large neat batches on the undersides of leaves of the foodplants, and hatch in ten to twelve days.

Larva
When newly hatched the larva is 1·5 mm long; the head is black and the body ochreous with black dorsal marks. When the larva is fully grown, the colour is variable – it may be brown or green. There is now a broken subdorsal line of black dashes on the abdominal segments, and the spiracles are black.

The eggshells are partly eaten. During the first instar the larva is a semi-looper, moving with a gait reminiscent of Geometrid larvae. It is one of the larvae referred to as 'cutworms' because, as it feeds in gardens at night, it often bites off the stems of herbaceous plants. During the day it rests beneath the surface of the soil and is frequently found by digging. It feeds throughout the winter except during very cold weather.

Pupa
The pupa is reddish-brown, smooth, and shiny. It is contained in a smooth-walled chamber in the soil, 2·5 to 5 cm below the surface. The adult emerges in three to four weeks.

NOCTUIDAE (HADENINAE) **The Lychnis**

Wingspan 30–40 mm

IMAGO ■
EGG ▦
LARVA ▨
PUPA ■

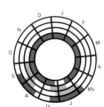

Distribution
Throughout the British Isles.

Habitat
A wide variety of habitats: wood-land, gardens and hedgerows – anywhere where the foodplants grow.

Life cycle
One generation a year, with a par-tial second generation in the south of England. Overwinters as a pupa.

Larval foodplants
The seeds of *Silene* and *Lychnis* spp., especially red campion (*Silene dioica*) and white campion (*S. alba*).

Imago
The forewings are greyish-brown mottled with dark brown and black, with a yellowish-white zig-zag submarginal line. The reniform and orbicular stigmata are outlined in white and almost touch at their lower ends. The hindwings are greyish-brown, becoming darker brown to-wards the outer margins. Sexes are similar, but the antennae of the female are more shortly pectinate than those of the male.

Variation can sometimes occur in the pattern of marks on the forewing and in the intensity of the ground colour.

Hadena bicruris (HUFNAGEL)

Egg on red campion

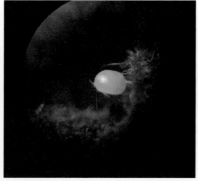

Egg; length 1 mm

Larval entrance hole

Larva inside seed capsule

Fully-grown larva; length 30 mm

Pupa; length 16 mm

This species may be distinguished from the Campion (*H. rivularis*) by the shape of the mark formed by the reniform and orbicular stigmata. In *H. rivularis* these marks join at their lower ends, whereas in *H. bicruris* they remain separated. The moth flies at night, visits flowers and is attracted to light.

Egg
The eggs are hemispherical, shiny with a finely pitted surface. When laid they are greenish-white, but become grey just prior to hatching. They are laid singly on the calyx of a flower of the food-plant, and hatch in about ten days.

Larva
The newly-hatched larva is 1·5 mm long, with a dark brown head and an ochreous body. When the larva is fully grown, the head is brown and the body ochreous with a white broken dorsal line and a series of dark brown dorsal V-shaped marks; there is a brown spiracular line.

The eggshell is not eaten. The young larva bores into the calyx of its foodplant and feeds on the developing seeds. It spins a plug of silk mixed with frass with which it closes the mouth of the seed capsule. Eventually the larva outgrows the seed capsule and may then be found resting on the outside, with its head poked inside.

Pupa
The pupa is light reddish-brown and shiny, with a slightly pitted surface and a prominent well-developed tongue case. It is enclosed in a thin silken cocoon beneath the surface of the ground. In those individuals which do not overwinter, the adult moth emerges in three to four weeks.

NOCTUIDAE (HADENINAE) **Pine Beauty**

Wingspan 32–40 mm

IMAGO
EGG
LARVA
PUPA

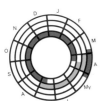

Distribution
Throughout the British Isles, but less common in Ireland.

Habitat
Coniferous woodland, and parks and gardens with conifers.

Life cycle
One generation a year. Overwinters as a pupa.

Larval foodplants
Pines (*Pinus* spp.), especially Scots Pine (*P. sylvestris*).

Imago
The forewings are reddish, shaded with reddish-brown, ochreous and white. The orbicular stigmata are white, and the reniform stigmata large and white with a reddish-ochreous centre. The hindwings are pinkish-brown. The sexes are similar, except in the antennae – the male's are fasciculate, and the female's very finely ciliate.

The most common variation is ab. *griseovariegata*, in which the ground colour of the wings is grey and the forewings are shaded with greenish-grey.

The moth flies at night, visits sallow blossom, and is attracted to light. By day it rests on pine trunks or branches.

Eggs; width 1 mm

2nd instar larvae; length 6 mm

Larva before final moult; length 30 mm

Fully-grown larva; length 38 mm

Pupa; length 16 mm

Egg

The eggs are hemispherical with a flattened base, strongly ribbed and faintly reticulated. When laid they are yellow, but they gradually develop a purplish-brown shading round the top portion. They are laid in short rows, either on the underside of pine needles or on the twigs at the base of the needles, and hatch in about two weeks.

Larva

When newly hatched the larva is 2·5 mm long; the head is pale brown and the body dark green. As the larva grows, it develops white longitudinal stripes. When it is fully grown, the head is brown, and the body dark green with white longitudinal stripes and a white and orange-brown spiracular stripe.

The eggshell is not eaten. When young the larva eats the youngest pine needles, and when older the more mature ones, starting at the tip and working towards the base. The colour and stripes provide marvellous camouflage among the pine needles, and if disturbed the larva drops in a rigid, straight position, resembling a fallen pine needle. Large numbers of these larvae are sometimes a pest in conifer plantations.

Pupa

The pupa is dark reddish-brown, and dull, with a slightly roughened surface. The larval skin remains attached to the cremaster. The pupa is enclosed in a thin cocoon either in a crevice in the bark or in surface litter such as fallen pine needles.

NOCTUIDAE (HADENINAE) **Hebrew Character**

Wingspan 30–40 mm

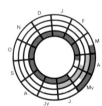

Distribution
Throughout the British Isles.

Habitat
Virtually any type of habitat is suitable.

Life cycle
One generation a year. Overwinters as a pupa.

Larval foodplants
Polyphagous – herbaceous plants, shrubs and deciduous trees. Special favourites are sallow (*Salix* spp.), hawthorn (*Crataegus monogyna*), oak (*Quercus* spp.), and dock (*Rumex* spp.).

Imago
The forewings are reddish-brown shaded with grey. In the centre of the forewing is the group of black marks which gives the moth its English name. The hindwings are grey-brown. The sexes are similar except for the antennae; those of the female are more weakly pectinate than those of the male.

Variation occurs in the ground colour of the forewings. In ab. *gothicina* the ground colour is reddish-brown and the black markings on the forewings are either absent or very faint.

The Hebrew Character is very common. The moths fly at night, eagerly visit sallow blossom, and are attracted to light, often in great numbers.

Egg
The eggs are hemispherical, ribbed and reticu-

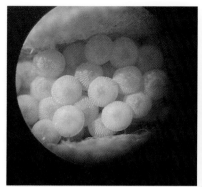

Eggs; width 0·75 mm   Fully-grown larva; length 40 mm   Pupa; length 15 mm

lated. When laid they are white, but after about three days brown marks develop – a patch at the micropyle, and a ring lower down. Just before hatching the eggs become blackish-grey. They are laid in large batches either on leaves of the food-plant or in bark crevices, and hatch in about two weeks.

Larva

When newly hatched the larva is 2 mm long, with a black head and ochreous body. After the first moult the head is brown and the body green with white stripes. When the larva is fully grown, the head is yellowish-green and the body grey-green with minute white dots; the dorsal and subdorsal lines are white, and the spiracular stripe black above and white below.

The eggshells are eaten. The larva feeds mainly at night, and if disturbed drops from the foodplant and rolls into a ring.

Pupa

The pupa is dark reddish-brown, tapers sharply towards the tail, and has a slightly roughened surface. It is contained in a thin silken cocoon beneath the surface of the ground.

NOCTUIDAE (CUCULLINAE) **The Mullein**

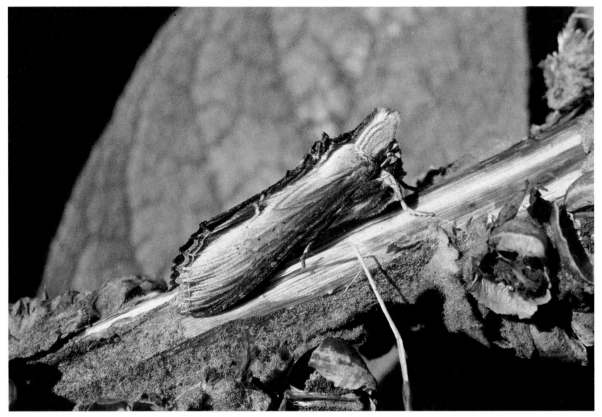

Wingspan 44–54 mm

IMAGO
EGG
LARVA
PUPA

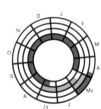

Distribution
England and Wales, as far north as Cumbria and Durham.

Habitat
Downland, open woodland, commons, waste ground, marshes, and gardens.

Life cycle
One generation a year. Overwinters as a pupa, sometimes for up to four years.

Larval foodplants
Mulleins, both wild and cultivated (*Verbascum* spp.), figworts (*Scrophularia* spp.), buddleias (*Buddleia* spp.).

Imago
The forewings are narrow and brownish-ochreous, with chocolate brown costas and inner margins. The outer margins are strongly dentated. The hindwings are small and greyish-brown. The thorax bears a prominent crest immediately behind the head, and this crest points forwards. The antennae are simple on the basal half, and then shortly ciliate to the tips. The sexes are similar, but males have an anal tuft which females lack.

Variation occurs frequently in the ground colour of the wings.

The moth flies at night and is attracted to light. During the day it rests on dead stems or twigs, when its resemblance to a piece of dry twig provides a marvellous camouflage.

Egg
The eggs are conical with a flattened base, ribbed,

Cucullia verbasci (LINNAEUS)

Egg on mullein

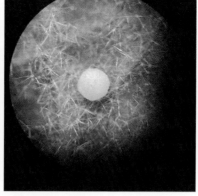
Egg; width 1 mm

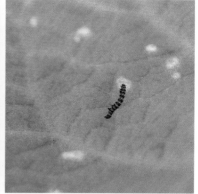
2nd instar larva; length 8 mm

Fully-grown larva; length 41 mm

Pupa; length 19 mm

and finely reticulated. They are white when laid, becoming pale yellow after a few days, and then grey just before hatching. They are laid singly on the underside of a leaf of the foodplant, usually on the layer of leaves above the basal leaf layer, and they hatch in ten to fourteen days.

Larva
When newly hatched the larva is 3 mm long; the head is brown and the body greenish-yellow with black tubercles bearing black hairs. It is a semi-looper at this stage. After the first moult the head is black and the body is banded alternately with white and dark grey. When the larva is fully grown, the head is yellow spotted with black, the body is white, sometimes tinged with very pale blue, and on each segment is a transverse yellow band spotted with black.

The eggshell is not eaten. During the early instars the larva eats small holes in the leaf, but in later stages the whole substance of the leaf is eaten. Larvae usually remain on the undersides of the leaves, and if disturbed fall to the ground and writhe about. Sometimes larvae may be found feeding on flowers, particularly of the great mullein (*V. thapsus*), and in recent years have often been found in gardens feeding on leaves of buddleias.

Pupa
The pupa is light reddish-brown with blackish spiracles. It is smooth and shiny except on the dorsal surface of the abdomen which is roughened and dull. The haustellum is very long, projecting two-thirds of the way down the abdomen. The pupa is contained in a very tough cocoon situated 5 to 10 cm beneath the surface of the ground, and may overwinter for up to four years.

NOCTUIDAE (CUCULLINAE) **Early Grey**

Wingspan 32–40 mm

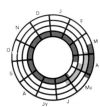

IMAGO
EGG
LARVA
PUPA

Distribution
Throughout the British Isles, but less common in Scotland.

Habitat
Open woodland, hedgerows, and gardens.

Life cycle
One generation a year. Overwinters as a pupa.

Larval foodplants
Honeysuckle (*Lonicera periclymenum*); also cultivated honeysuckles.

Imago
The forewings are grey with a pattern of darker grey and black. The stigmata are large, and joined to form a U-shape. The hindwings are grey with darker veins. There is a small dorsal crest on the first abdominal segment. The sexes are similar, except that the antennae of the male are shortly ciliate and those of the female very thinly so.

Variation occurs very frequently in the shade of grey forming the ground colour. In ab. *rosea* the forewing is flushed with pink.

The moths fly at night, visit sallow blossom, and are attracted to light. During the day they may be found sitting low down on tree trunks, fences, or gate posts.

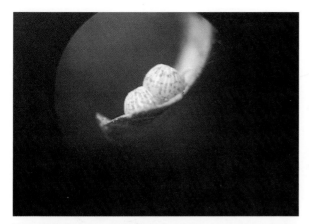

Eggs; height 1 mm

Larva in May; length 20 mm

Fully-grown larva; length 40 mm

Pupa; length 16 mm

Egg

The eggs are rounded with a flattened top and base, ribbed, and reticulated. When laid they are white, but after two days a pattern of brown mottling develops. They are laid singly or in pairs on the stems or leaves of the foodplant, and hatch in fourteen to eighteen days.

Larva

When newly hatched the larva is 3·5 mm long; the head is ochreous and the body greyish-ochreous. When the larva is fully grown the head and body are brownish-ochreous, the dorsal line is yellowish, interrupted by a black mark on the seventh segment, and the spiracular line is brown and yellow.

The eggshell is not eaten. During the first instar the larva rests either on a stem or on the edge of a leaf, and if disturbed falls off and hangs on a silken thread. At first it eats small holes in the leaves, but when older it consumes the whole leaf. The larva feeds at night, and during later instars rests on stems during the day – it is very well camouflaged, as its colour matches that of the honeysuckle stems.

Pupa

The pupa is reddish-brown, slightly shiny, and smooth except for raised transverse bands on the dorsal surface of the abdominal segments. It is contained in a very tough cocoon formed below the surface of the ground. The larva remains inside the cocoon for several weeks before pupating.

♂ wingspan 38–46 mm

♀ wingspan 38–46 mm

IMAGO
EGG
LARVA
LARVA IN COCOON
PUPA

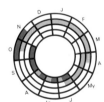

■ Distribution
Throughout the British Isles.

■ Habitat
Bushy places, hedgerows, and woodland.

Life cycle
One generation a year. Over-winters as an egg.

Larval foodplants
Hawthorn (*Crataegus monogyna*), and blackthorn (*Prunus spinosa*). Also recorded on wild cherry (*P. avium*).

Imago
In the typical form the forewings are pale reddish-brown, suffused with metallic green, and with fine black transverse lines. The hindwings are brownish-grey. The sexes are similar, but the antennae of the male are dentate while those of the female are ciliate. In ab. *capucina*, the forewing is dark brown, without the green suffusion, and the hindwings are brown.

Variation occurs commonly, producing a range of colouring between the two forms described above.

The moth flies at night, visits ivy blossom and ripe blackberries, and is attracted to light. The dark form *capucina* is most often seen in industrial areas.

Egg
The eggs are conical, strongly ribbed, and finely reticulated. When laid they are yellow, but after about a week they become yellowish-ochreous marked with purplish-brown mottling between the ribs. They are laid either singly or in small clusters among buds or in crevices in the bark of the foodplants.

Egg; height 0·9 mm

3rd instar larva; length 16 mm

Eggs on hawthorn

Fully-grown larva; length 42 mm

Pupa; length 17 mm

Larva

When newly hatched the larva is 3 mm long; the head is brown and the body brownish-ochreous with dark brown longitudinal lines. During the first instar it is a semi-looper. By the third instar the head is reddish-brown and the body blackish-brown with an oblique orange lateral mark on the first abdominal segment and a prominent dorsal hump on the last segment. When the larva is fully grown the head is reddish-brown and the body grey-brown with an orange-red lateral mark on the first abdominal segment and a hump on the last segment; the ground colour of the larva varies, and may also be green or dark brown.

The eggshell is not eaten. The larva emerges from the egg during April, and at first feeds on buds, later graduating to leaves. When young it hangs on a silken thread if disturbed – an older larva will drop from the foodplant and whip from side to side. It feeds at night, and during the day rests on twigs.

Pupa

The pupa is golden brown, shiny, slightly roughened on the thorax and abdomen, and blackish between the segments. It is enclosed in a very tough cocoon beneath the surface of the ground. The larva rests inside the cocoon for up to two months before pupating.

NOCTUIDAE (ACRONICTINAE) **The Miller**

Wingspan 38–45 mm

IMAGO
EGG
LARVA
PUPA

Distribution
England and Wales. Less common in Scotland; in Ireland mainly confined to coastal districts.

Habitat
Heathland, moorland, and woodland – wherever birch is found.

Life cycle
One generation a year. Overwinters – sometimes more than once – as a pupa.

Larval foodplants
Mainly birch (*Betula* spp.). Also recorded on poplar (*Populus* spp.), alder (*Alnus glutinosa*), aspen (*Populus tremula*), sallow (*Salix* spp.), and oak (*Quercus* spp.).

Imago
The forewings are white, finely dusted with black scales, and with a few black spots, short black lines, and a black basal streak. The hindwings are white with a terminal line of grey spots. The sexes are similar, the antennae of both male and female being very shortly ciliate.

Variation is common. The above description refers to the most widespread form in Britain, f. *grisea*. It occurs most frequently in Scotland and Ireland and is white with little or no dark marking. A melanic form, ab. *melanocephala*, with a black thorax and heavily suffused forewings occurs in industrial areas of the Midlands and northern England.

The moth flies at night, becoming active at dusk. It visits flowers and is attracted to light.

Egg
The egg is slightly conical with a wide flat base

Acronicta leporina (LINNAEUS)

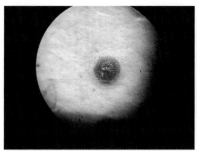

Egg; width 1·5 mm

3rd instar larva; length 9 mm

5th instar larva; length 19 mm

6th instar larva; length 22 mm

Fully-grown larva; length 32 mm

Pupa; length 17 mm

projecting as a rim, and with numerous ribs. It is shiny, and when laid is pale primrose yellow in colour. After about four days the raised centre becomes brown and the rim round the base colourless. Eggs are laid singly on leaves or twigs of the foodplant, and hatch in about ten days.

Larva

When newly hatched the larva is 2 mm long; the head is black, and the body is marked with alternate bands of dark brown and ochreous and bears long dark hairs. After the second moult the body is ochreous marked with black, and the hairs are long, pale, and straight. Following the third moult the body is pale green with raised black dorsal tubercles; the hairs are still long and straight. After the fourth moult the black tubercles bear tufts of black bristles, and the long hairs are beginning to curve. When the larva is fully grown the head and body are pale green with a few tufts of black bristles on the back. The whole body is concealed by the long hairs, which curve forwards on the right side of the body, and backwards on the left. These hairs are now usually white, but particular-

ly in northern districts, yellow-haired individuals may be found.

The eggshell is not eaten. During the early instars the larva eats only the cuticle of the leaf, usually of the underside, but later the whole leaf is eaten. It feeds mainly at night. When not feeding it rests, usually on the underside of a leaf, in a curled position, the long hairs concealing the body and giving it a resemblance to a spider's nest or lump of fluff. When about to pupate, the body goes brownish and the hairs become dishevelled.

Pupa

The pupa is shiny, dark reddish-brown with a greenish tinge on the wingcases, and slightly roughened on the abdominal segments. It is extremely active, and if disturbed will twitch and roll about. It is attached by tail hooks to the interior of a cocoon which is usually situated in a bark crevice. It may overwinter more than once.

Breeding

A piece of rotten wood or deeply creviced bark should be provided as a pupation site.

NOCTUIDAE (AMPHIPYRINAE) **Angle Shades**

Wingspan 45–55 mm

IMAGO
EGG
LARVA
PUPA

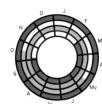

Distribution
Throughout the British Isles, but less common in Scotland.

Habitat
Hedgerows, woodland, gardens, and waste ground.

Life cycle
At least two generations a year. Overwinters as a larva.

Larval foodplants
A wide variety of plants, including dock (*Rumex* spp.), dandelion (*Taraxacum* spp.), chickweed (*Stellaria* spp.), nettle (*Urtica* spp.), bramble (*Rubus* spp.), and ivy (*Hedera helix*). Can be a pest in greenhouses, eating foliage of a variety of plants including tomatoes and streptocarpus.

Imago
The forewing is long and narrow with a scalloped termen, and is shaded with reddish-ochreous and olive brown. In the central area is a reddish-olive V-shaped mark. The hindwing is ochreous shaded with darker brown. There are prominent thoracic and abdominal crests. The sexes are similar, although the antennae of the male are shortly ciliate and those of the female simple.

Variation can occur in the shade of the ground colour, which may be suffused with rose pink. Sometimes the V-mark is darker red.

There are at least two generations a year, and numbers are reinforced by immigrants from Europe, so the moth has been recorded in every month of the year. However, peak flight times are usually from late May to the end of June, and September and early October. The moth flies at night, visits flowers and fruit such as blackberries, and is attracted to light. During the day it rests in the undergrowth or on tree trunks with the wings folded in a characteristic manner.

Eggs; width 0·75 mm

3rd instar larva; length 11 mm

Fully-grown larva (green form)

Fully-grown larva (brown form); length 35 mm

Pupa; length 18 mm

Egg

The egg is dome-shaped, strongly ribbed and reticulated, and glistening. When laid it is pale yellow in colour, but after two or three days the top becomes mottled with reddish-brown, with a ring of the same colour just below that area, and just before hatching the whole egg becomes dark grey. Eggs are laid singly or in batches on either side of leaves of the foodplant, and hatch in about ten days.

Larva

When newly hatched the larva is 2 mm long; the head is brownish-green and the body greenish-ochreous with darker bands. After the first moult the head is yellowish and the body green with a white spiracular line and a fine interrupted white dorsal line; the segmental divisions are yellow. When the larva is fully grown its colour is variable. It may be light brown with darker brown V-shaped marks, or it may be yellowish-green with darker green V-marks. In either case it retains the white spiracular line and interrupted white dorsal line.

The eggshell is not eaten. When newly hatched the larva is a semi-looper, possessing only three pairs of prolegs. It feeds at night, and overwinters, feeding slowly right through this period, becoming fully grown in March.

Pupa

The pupa is deep reddish-brown, with darker segmental divisions. Although very slightly roughened, the surface feels smooth, and is shiny. The pupa is enclosed in a thin, oval cocoon just beneath the surface of the ground, and the adult emerges in four to six weeks.

♂ wingspan 40–45 mm

♀ wingspan 48–54 mm

IMAGO
EGG
LARVA
PUPA

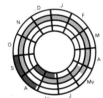

Distribution
England, Wales, Ireland, and southern and eastern Scotland.

Habitat
Ponds, marshy places, fens and ditches where bulrush grows.

Life cycle
One generation a year. Over-winters as an egg.

Larval foodplants
Bulrush (*Typha latifolia*). Sometimes lesser bulrush (*T. angustifolia*).

Imago
In the male the forewings are reddish-ochreous, shaded with brown and with white veins. To-wards the outer margin is a row of black wedge-shaped marks. The hindwings are whitish-ochreous shaded with brown towards the margin. The antennae are setose. The forewings of the female are whitish-ochreous but are otherwise similar to those of the male, as are the hindwings. Females are usually larger than males and their antennae are very finely setose.

Variation occurs in the ground colour of the wings of both sexes. In ab. *fraterna* the forewing is deep reddish-brown or blackish.

The moth flies at night, becoming active at dusk. It does not feed, but is attracted to light. During the day it rests among the dead bulrush leaves, where its colouring provides an excellent camouflage.

Egg
The egg is almost spherical and the surface bears slight reticulations. It is creamy-white in colour, becoming brownish just before hatching.

The tip of the female's abdomen is furnished with a pair of chitinous 'cutters'. When egg-laying, she settles on a bulrush stem and with a slight rocking motion uses these cutters to make a slit through the plant's epidermis – a faint scratch-ing is audible as she does this. She then inserts her ovipositor through the slit and deposits a single egg inside a cell of the bulrush. Sap exudes from the slit for a short time, and subsequently a small vertical blackish scar indicates the presence of an egg within. The eggs overwinter, and hatch around the beginning of May.

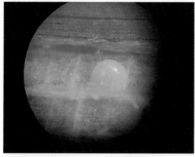

Egg; width 1 mm

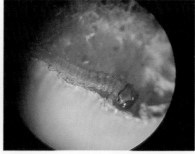

Newly-hatched larva; length 4 mm

'Window'; diameter 8 mm

Fully-grown larva; length 50 mm

Pupa in stem

Pupa; length 30 mm

Larva

When newly hatched the larva has a brown dorsal surface, with black dots and short black hairs, and the head and collar on the second segment are brown. The ventral surface is ochreous. When fully grown the larva is long and slender. The body is pinkish-ochreous, slightly darker on the back, and with black spiracles. The head and prothoracic plate are reddish-brown, the anal plate blackish-brown.

The eggshell is not eaten. The larva feeds within a stem of the bulrush, inside a tunnel which becomes packed with frass. The presence of a well-grown larva in a stem may be detected by the yellowing of the leaves and failure of the plant to flower. Affected stems are often pecked by moorhens and coots to extract larvae and pupae.

Pupa

The pupa is slender and cylindrical. Its colour is reddish-brown, darker between the segments, and its surface is dull and slightly roughened. When ready to pupate, the larva chews through the plant tissue, leaving a layer of epidermis intact – this circular 'window' may be found by peeling away the outer layer of leaves. The larva pupates head downwards in its tunnel just above the 'window', through which the adult moth emerges after about four weeks, leaving the empty pupa case within the stem.

NOCTUIDAE (AMPHIPYRINAE) **Fen Wainscot**

Wingspan 32–36 mm

IMAGO	■
EGG	▨
LARVA	▨
PUPA	■

Distribution
Eastern and southern England, Lancashire and Cumbria.

Habitat
Reed-beds.

Life cycle
One generation a year. Over-winters as an egg.

Larval foodplant
Common reed (*Phragmites australis*).

Imago
The forewings are creamy-ochreous, faintly shaded with brown towards the outer margin. The hindwings are brownish with paler veins. The head and front of the thorax are white, and there is a thoracic crest. The sexes are similar, but the female's antennae are more sparsely ciliate than those of the male.

Variation occurs in the extent of the brown shading on the forewing. In ab. *rufescens* there is a rich reddish suffusion.

The moth flies at night, feeds from the flowers of marsh grasses, and is attracted to light. It becomes active at dusk, and during the day rests concealed among the reed stems.

Egg
The eggs are slightly conical, but appear very flattened, with numerous fine ribs. When newly laid they are pale lemon yellow, but become reddish-buff after twenty-four hours, and dark

Eggs in reed sheath

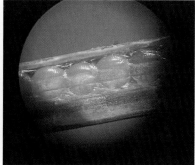

Eggs; width 1 mm

Newly-hatched larva; length 2·5 mm

Fully-grown larva; length 22 mm

Larval exit hole; diameter 2 mm

Pupa; length 16 mm

grey just before hatching.

The female becomes active and commences laying at dusk. Having selected a reed, she inserts her ovipositor into a leaf sheath with a slight rocking movement and deposits eggs in a row inside the sheath. Having overwintered, they hatch the following May.

Larva

When newly hatched the larva has an ochreous body with brown transverse bands, and a black head and prothoracic collar. At this stage it is a semi-looper. When the larva is fully grown, the head is black and the prothoracic and anal plates dark brown. The body is whitish-ochreous with a few black dots and a purplish blotch on the dorsal surface of each abdominal segment.

The eggshell is not eaten. The young larva enters the reed stem through a hole bored just above a node. It then eats its way upwards, forming a tunnel which becomes packed with frass. When fully grown it chews a circular hole at the top of the tunnel and leaves the stem prior to pupation. Affected stems become dried as the shoot dies, and are very conspicuous.

Pupa

The smooth, shiny pupa is reddish-brown, darker between the segments. It is formed in a thin cocoon among debris on the surface of the ground, and the adult emerges in about three weeks.

NOCTUIDAE (HELIOTHINAE) **Shoulder-striped Clover**

Wingspan 32–36 mm

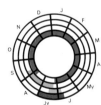

IMAGO
EGG
LARVA
PUPA

Distribution
Heaths in Dorset, Hampshire and Surrey; very local populations.

Habitat
Damp heathland.

Life cycle
One generation a year. Over-winters as a pupa.

Larval foodplants
The flowers of cross-leaved heath (*Erica tetralix*). Also recorded on the seed heads of bog asphodel (*Narthecium ossifragum*) and flowers of heather (*Calluna vulgaris*).

Imago
The forewing is brownish-ochreous, spotted and banded with black. The presence of a black basal streak distinguishes this species from the Marbled Clover (*H. viriplaca*). The hindwing is cream-coloured, blotched and shaded with black. The sexes are similar, but the antennae of the male are slightly ciliate while those of the female are simple.

Variation can occur in the ground colour of the forewing, which may be more olive in some individuals.

The moth flies by day in sunshine, and in flight much resembles the Silver Y (*A. gamma*). It visits flowers, particularly those of heaths and heather, and is occasionally attracted to light.

Egg
The egg is domed, ribbed, and reticulated. When laid the colour is yellow, but after a couple of days a reddish-brown ring develops round the 'shoulders'. It is laid singly, tucked in among the

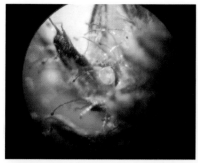

Egg; height 0·5 mm

4th instar larva; length 10 mm

Larva before final moult; length 23 mm

Fully-grown larva (brown form);
length 32 mm

Fully-grown larva

Pupa; length 18 mm

flowers and buds of the foodplant, and hatches in seven to nine days.

Larva

When newly hatched the larva is 1·5 mm long; the head and prothoracic plate are black and the body ochreous. By the third instar, the ground colour has become greenish, and after the third moult the body is dark green with longitudinal stripes of black and white. When the larva is fully grown, the body is long and slender, with short bristles. There are now two colour forms. In the most frequent, the head and prothoracic plate are yellowish-green freckled with black, and the ground colour is very dark olive green. The spiracular line is yellowish-white, and below it is a broad wavy white and brown stripe. In the second colour form, the head and prothoracic plate are reddish-brown freckled with black and the ground colour purplish-brown; the spiracular line is yellow, and the wavy stripe beneath it white and brown as in the common form.

Most of the eggshell is eaten. During the first two instars, any disturbance causes the larva to drop from the foodplant and hang by a thread of silk. It feeds mainly at night, except just before pupation, when it also feeds by day.

Pupa

The pupa is slender, smooth and shiny. The thorax and wingcases are yellowish-green, and the abdomen reddish-brown, darker between the segments. There is a dark brown medio-dorsal stripe, and the cremaster bears two straight parallel spines. The pupa is formed below the surface of the soil.

NOCTUIDAE (ACONTIINAE) **Silver Hook**

Wingspan 23–28 mm

IMAGO
EGG
LARVA
PUPA

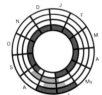

Distribution
Local in suitable habitats in England, Wales, Ireland and western Scotland.

Habitat
Boggy heathland, marshes and fens.

Life cycle
Usually one generation a year, but occasionally specimens are reported in August – it is uncertain whether these represent a partial second generation or have emerged late from the earlier generation. Overwinters as a pupa.

Larval foodplants
Cotton-grasses (*Eriophorum* spp.). Also recorded on wood-sedge (*Carex sylvatica*) and other sedges.

Imago
The forewing is olive brown with a broad greyish-cream streak along the costa and the outer margin. The reniform stigma is greyish-cream and projects downwards from the costal streak. The hindwings are greyish-brown. The sexes are similar, but the antennae of the male are slightly ciliate and those of the female are simple.

Variation can sometimes occur in the ground colour of the forewing, which may be tinged with reddish.

The Silver Hook gets its English name from the hook-shaped reniform stigma on the forewing. It flies at night, becoming active at dusk, and is attracted to light. During the day it may be disturbed quite readily from grass tussocks, where it rests at the bases of the stems.

Egg
The eggs are domed, weakly ribbed and reticulated, and shiny. When laid they are white in

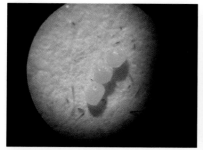

Eggs; width 0·6 mm

Eggshells on cotton-grass

Pupa in moss

Pupa; length 9 mm

Fully-grown larva; length 24 mm

colour, but after three days they become yellow, and then grey just before hatching. They are laid in short rows along the midrib on the upper surface of leaves of the foodplant, and hatch in about ten days.

Larva

When newly hatched the larva is 1·5 mm long; the head is brown and the body ochreous with short hairs. After feeding commences, the ground colour changes to a shade of green, which deepens with each moult. When the larva is fully grown the head is yellowish-green and the body green with a darker dorsal line, white subdorsal lines and a yellow spiracular line. The segmental divisions are yellow. There are two pairs of fully developed ventral prolegs, and a rudimentary third pair.

The eggshell is not eaten. During the first instar, if disturbed the larva hangs from a silken thread, but in later instars it drops from the foodplant and rolls into a knot. It feeds only at night, except during the last instar when it is also active by day. When fully grown it eats notches out of the side of the foodplant leaves.

Pupa

The pupa is shiny with a slightly roughened surface. The thorax and wingcases are greenish and the abdomen greenish-brown, darker between the segments. The larval skin remains attached to the cremaster. The pupa is contained in a fairly open-work but tough cocoon of brown silk in sphagnum or other moss beneath the foodplant.

NOCTUIDAE (CHLOEPHORINAE) **Cream-bordered Green Pea**

Wingspan 20–24 mm

IMAGO
EGG
LARVA
PUPA

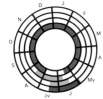

Distribution
Eastern England as far north as Yorkshire, and southern England from Kent to Dorset. Has been recorded from southern Lancashire.

Habitat
Damp woodland, osier beds, marshy places, fenland and river valleys.

Life cycle
One generation a year, and also sometimes a partial second generation in August. Overwinters as a pupa.

Larval foodplants
Various species of willows, especially osier (*Salix viminalis*), creeping willow (*S. repens*), and goat willow (*S. caprea*).

Imago
The forewing is pea-green, becoming slightly darker at the outer margin, with a white costal streak. The hindwing, head and abdomen are white, and the thorax is green. The antennae are shortly ciliate. The sexes are similar.

Variation is uncommon, but occasionally the green of the forewings may be slightly yellowish.

This species can be confused very easily with the Green Oak Tortrix (*Tortrix viridana*). The latter species lacks the white costa and has a grey hindwing. The Cream-bordered Green Pea flies at night, beginning at dusk, and is attracted to light.

Egg
The eggs are dome-shaped, strongly ribbed and faintly reticulated. They are whitish, with a chocolate brown area surrounding the sunken micropyle. There is also a chocolate brown ring on the 'shoulders'. The eggs are laid singly, in pairs or in short rows, usually on the underside of leaves of the foodplant, and they hatch in about seven days.

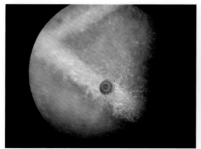

Egg; width 0·5 mm

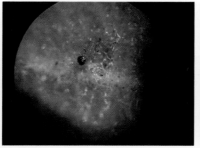

Newly-hatched larva; length 0·9 mm

Fully-grown larva; length 13 mm

Cocoon; length 10 mm

Pupa; length 8 mm

Larva

When newly hatched the larva has a black head and black prothoracic and anal plates, and the body is ochreous with long pale hairs. When the larva is fully grown its body tapers from the second abdominal segment to the tail; the ground colour is greenish-white, with a broad subdorsal line and fine lateral and spiracular lines, all reddish-brown. There are prominent dorsal humps on the second and eighth abdominal segments.

The eggshell is not eaten. During the first instar the larva bores into the leaf and feeds concealed between the upper and lower cuticles. In later instars it fastens the tip of a shoot together with silk, and feeds inside this shelter.

Pupa

The pupa is fat and not shiny. Along the whole length of the dorsal surface is a broad reddish-purple stripe. The wingcases are greenish and the rest of the body is brown. The abdomen bears minute dorsal spines. The pupa is contained in an extremely tough boat-shaped cocoon of greyish-brown silk attached to a twig of the foodplant.

NOCTUIDAE (CHLOEPHORINAE) **Scarce Silver-lines**

Wingspan 40–48 mm

IMAGO
EGG
LARVA
PUPA

Distribution
Wales, and England as far north as Cumbria and South Yorkshire. Commoner in the southern districts of its range.

Habitat
Woodland and parkland with oaks.

Life cycle
One generation a year. Over-winters as a young larva.

Larval foodplant
Oak (*Quercus* spp.).

Imago
The green forewing is crossed by two parallel oblique yellowish-white lines. The hindwing and abdomen are white, and the head and thorax green. The antennae, which are thickly ciliate in the male and sparsely ciliate in the female, are yellow, shaded with red near the base on the dorsal surface. Females are often slightly larger than males.

Variation is rare – very occasionally there may be a slight difference in the ground colour of the forewings.

The moth flies at night, becoming active at dusk, and is attracted to light.

Bena prasinana (LINNAEUS)

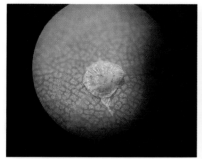

Egg; width 1·5 mm

Larva before hibernation; length 8 mm

Fully-grown larva; length 28 mm

Cocoon; length 20 mm

Pupa; length 18 mm

Egg

The egg is shaped like a shallow wide-based cone, ribbed and reticulated. When laid it is whitish, but after about two days a pattern of light brown marks develops. Eggs are laid singly on leaves of the foodplant, usually on the underside, and hatch in about ten days.

Larva

When newly hatched the larva is 2·25 mm long and ochreous in colour, with dense pale hairs. After feeding it becomes greener, and in the second instar it also has some yellow marks. During hibernation its colour is grey-brown. When the larva is fully grown, its body tapers to the anal claspers from a prominent dorsal thoracic hump; the head is green and usually retracted under the thoracic segments and the body is yellowish-green with a yellow spiracular line and oblique yellow lateral lines.

The eggshell is not eaten. The young larva feeds until about the end of September, and then takes up position for hibernation among the oak buds. Feeding resumes in spring, and the larva becomes fully grown towards the end of May. It feeds mainly at night, and during the day rests on the underside of a leaf.

Pupa

The pupa is slightly rough in texture and bright green in colour, with a broad dorsal row of black marks. The abdominal segments have small black dorsal spines. The pupa is contained in a tough boat-shaped cocoon of pale yellowish silk with longitudinal ridges which converge to form a pointed projection at the head end. The cocoon is spun on the underside of an oak leaf, and the adult moth emerges in three to four weeks.

NOCTUIDAE (SARROTHRIPINAE) **Oak Nycteoline**

Wingspan 24–30 mm

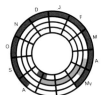

IMAGO
EGG
LARVA
PUPA

Distribution
Throughout the British Isles, though commoner in southern Britain.

Habitat
Woodland with oaks.

Life cycle
One generation a year. Overwinters as an adult.

Larval foodplant
Oak (*Quercus* spp.).

Imago
The forewings are extremely varied in their pattern and in their colour, which ranges from pale grey to purplish-brown and blackish. The hindwings are brownish-grey. The costa of the forewing is strongly arched near the base. The sexes are similar, except that the antennae of the male are very shortly ciliate and those of the female are simple.

Variation is very common, and between thirty and forty distinct forms have been named. In industrial areas a melanic form occurs (ab. *nigricans*).

The moth flies at night, becoming active to-

Half-grown larva; length 12 mm

Fully-grown larva; length 20 mm

Cocoon; length 12 mm

Pupa; length 10 mm

wards dusk, and comes occasionally to light. In the autumn it feeds at ivy blossom and over-ripe fruit such as blackberries. It hibernates in thick undergrowth or in evergreens such as pine, yew, holly, and ivy, becoming active again in spring.

Egg
Apparently undescribed.

Larva
During the earlier instars, the head and body are yellowish-green; the body bears long, fine, whitish hairs, there is a dark green dorsal line, and the segmental divisions are yellow. When fully grown the yellowish shade of the body and of the segmental divisions is much paler.

The larva feeds mainly at night except in the final instar, when it will also feed by day.

Pupa
The body of the pupa is pale green with a broad purplish-brown dorsal stripe, purplish-brown eyes, and whitish wingcases. It is contained in a tough cocoon of white silk shaped like an up-turned boat, which is situated either on the underside of an oak leaf, or between two adjacent leaves. The adult moth emerges in about two weeks.

NOCTUIDAE (PANTHEINAE) **Nut-tree Tussock**

Wingspan 30–38 mm

IMAGO ■
EGG ▪
LARVA ▪
PUPA ■

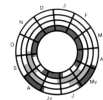

Distribution
Throughout the British Isles, though commonest in southern England and Wales.

Habitat
Woodland and hedgerows.

Life cycle
Two generations a year in southern Britain; one generation in the north, producing adult moths in June and July. Overwinters as a pupa.

Larval foodplants
A variety of trees, especially hazel (*Corylus avellana*), beech (*Fagus sylvatica*), birch (*Betula* spp.). Also recorded on hornbeam (*Carpinus betulus*), field maple (*Acer campestre*), and oak (*Quercus* spp.).

Imago
The basal half of the forewing is grey-brown or reddish-brown, and the outer half pale grey or brownish-grey. The round orbicular stigma is white, outlined with near-black. There is a wavy submarginal line. The hindwings are pale brown with a darker terminal band. The body has dorsal crests. The sexes are similar, except that the antennae of the male are bipectinate, and those of the female are shortly ciliate.

Variation occurs frequently in the ground colour of the forewings. Specimens from the Burren in Ireland are paler in colour and larger than the English form. A melanic variety, ab. *melanotica*, occurs in parts of southern England.

The moth flies at night, and males are attracted to light and will feed at sugar. Females are much more sluggish, and do not seem to be attracted by either sugar or light.

Egg
The eggs are hemispherical, ribbed, and reticu-

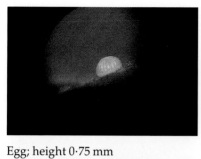

Egg; height 0·75 mm

Larval home

Larva in June; length 15 mm

Half-grown larva; length 20 mm

Fully-grown larva; length 29 mm

Fully-grown larva

Fully-grown larva

Fully-grown larva

Pupa; length 15 mm

lated. When laid they are yellowish-green in colour, but red equatorial marks appear after about two weeks, and the eggs become blackish before hatching. They are laid singly on the underside of leaves of the foodplant, and hatch after about two and a half weeks. While laying, the wings of the female quiver continually.

Larva

When newly hatched the larva is 2 mm long; the head is black and the body reddish-ochreous with long dark hairs. When fully grown, the larva is tremendously variable. The ground colour may be yellowish-ochreous, brownish-orange, whitish-ochreous, or reddish-ochreous. On most colour forms there is a conspicuous broken black dorsal stripe, and finer blackish lateral stripes. All colour

forms have two forward-pointing 'pencils' of long hairs on the first segment, and shorter tufts of hair dorsally on the first, second, and eighth abdominal segments. These tufts and pencils may be black or orange. In addition, the body is covered with tufts of whitish hairs.

The eggshell is not eaten. The larva forms a home for itself either by fastening two adjacent leaves together with silk, or by folding over the edge of a leaf and fastening this with silk. It emerges from its shelter to feed at night.

Pupa

The pupa is blackish-brown, slightly roughened and very shiny. It is enclosed in an open-work cocoon of thin brown silk mixed with a few larval hairs, and situated in litter beneath the foodplant.

NOCTUIDAE (PLUSIINAE) **Burnished Brass**

Wingspan 35–44 mm

IMAGO
EGG
LARVA
PUPA

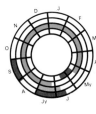

Distribution
Throughout the British Isles.

Habitat
Woodland, waste ground, commons, gardens, and hedgerows.

Life cycle
Two generations a year in southern Britain, the second a partial one. One generation a year in northern districts, producing adult moths in July and August. Overwinters as a young larva.

Larval foodplants
Common nettle (*Urtica dioica*). Also recorded on dead-nettle (*Lamium* spp.), and spear mint (*Mentha spicata*).

Imago
The forewing is purplish-brown with two metallic gold bands, and the hindwing is greyish-brown. There are prominent dorsal crests on the thorax and abdomen. The sexes are similar, but the antennae of the male are more densely ciliated than those of the female.

Variation occurs in the shade of the metallic bands, which may be greenish-gold, and in some individuals the two bands are joined across the central area of the forewing.

The moth flies at night, becoming active just before dusk, visits flowers, and is attracted to light. During the day it may be disturbed from foliage or undergrowth.

Egg
The egg is dome-shaped, lightly ribbed, and reticulated, with a very thin shell. It is white when laid, becoming slightly greyish before hatching.

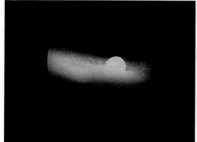

Egg; height 0·5 mm

Larva in April; length 20 mm

Fully-grown larva; length 30 mm

Pupa; length 22 mm

Cocoon

Eggs are laid singly on leaves of the foodplant, and hatch after eight to ten days.

Larva

When newly hatched the larva is 2 mm long, greyish-ochreous in colour, and a semi-looper. After feeding commences, its colour becomes greener. When the larva is fully grown, the head and body are green, the dorsal area of the body is patterned with white, and the spiracular line is white. The body bears numerous short dark hairs, and there are only three pairs of prolegs.

The eggshell is not eaten. The young larvae hibernate among dead leaves and litter on the surface of the ground, and begin feeding again in April. They feed mainly at night, and when resting keep the front portion of the body slightly humped.

Pupa

The pupa is black, smooth and shiny. It is formed within a cocoon of fine whitish silk on the underside of a foodplant leaf the edges of which have been drawn up round it with silk. The adult moth emerges in about four weeks.

NOCTUIDAE (PLUSIINAE) **Golden Plusia**

Wingspan 38–45 mm

IMAGO
EGG
LARVA
PUPA

Distribution
England, Wales, southern Scotland, and a few localities in County Dublin.

Habitat
Gardens.

Life cycle
There is normally one generation a year, but in southern England there may be a partial second generation, producing moths in September. Overwinters as a young larva.

Larval foodplants
Cultivated species of delphinium and monkshood.

Imago
The forewing is pale gold, with lighter and darker shading, and brown veins and transverse lines. The reniform stigma is enlarged to form a silver figure 8. The hindwing is grey-brown, shaded darker towards the margin. The thorax and abdomen bear prominent dorsal crests. The sexes are similar, but the antennae of the male are more densely ciliate than those of the female.

Variation can occur in the shade of the ground colour.

The moth flies at night, becoming active at dusk, and is attracted to light. It visits such flowers as delphiniums, buddleia and red valerian, and feeds with its wings vibrating continuously.

Egg
The eggs are hemispherical, ribbed and reticulated. Creamy-white when laid, they become grey

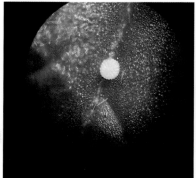

Egg; width 0·75 mm

(*Left*) Larva after hibernation, length 7 mm; (*right*) half-grown larva, length 15 mm

Fully-grown larva; length 30 mm

Larval home

Cocoon; length 29 mm

Pupa; length 20 mm

just before hatching. They are laid singly on the upper surface of leaves of the foodplant, and hatch in about eight days.

Larva
When newly hatched the larva is 2 mm long. During the early instars the head is black and the body blackish-green. Immediately after hibernation, the body is green with large black tubercles each bearing a short dark bristle. After the next moult the head and prothoracic plate are black and the body green with black dots and faint white lines. When the larva is fully grown the head and body are green with a white line above the spiracles. There are a few short whitish hairs and only three pairs of prolegs.

The eggshell is not eaten. The young larva hibernates at the base of the plant, and in spring begins to feed on the developing shoots, causing damage to the flower spikes. When older, the larva spins the edges of a leaf together with silk and lives inside the tent thus formed.

Pupa
The pupa is roughened and shiny, with a well-developed haustellum. Its dorsal surface is blackish-brown, and its wingcases and the ventral surface of its abdomen are green. It is enclosed in a golden-yellow cocoon of two layers – the outer strong and close-textured and the inner much finer – attached to a leaf of the foodplant, usually on the underside. The adult moth emerges in about four weeks.

NOCTUIDAE (PLUSIINAE) **Silver Y**

Wingspan 32–50 mm

IMAGO
EGG
LARVA
PUPA

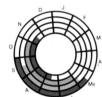

Distribution
Throughout the British Isles.

Habitat
Almost any type of habitat is suitable.

Life cycle
Usually two or three generations a year. Early stages are killed by frost in the autumn; there have been a few reports of adult moths over-wintering, but these cases are exceptional.

Larval foodplants
Polyphagous; has been recorded on virtually every species of low-growing plant, both wild and cultivated.

Imago
The forewing is greyish-brown, shaded with purple and white. In the central area is a silver Y, or 'gamma' mark. The hindwing is greyish-brown with a darker marginal band. The thorax and abdomen bear dorsal crests. The sexes are similar, but the antennae of the male are more densely ciliate than those of the female.

Variation is very common, both in the depth of colour on the forewing, and in the size – dwarf specimens often occur, known as ab. *gammina*.

The Silver Y is a very common immigrant from mainland Europe. The earliest arrivals usually reach our shores in May, and further influxes take place through the summer and early autumn. There is some evidence of a return migration in autumn. The early stages cannot survive our winter. The moth flies in sunshine and also at night; it visits flowers and is drawn to light.

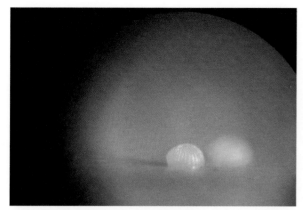

Egg; height 0·5 mm

Larva in September; length 20 mm

Fully-grown larva; length 30 mm

Pupa; length 20 mm

Egg

The eggs are dome-shaped, ribbed, and reticulated, with a very thin shell. White when laid, they become grey just before hatching. They are laid singly or in pairs on a leaf of the foodplant, usually on the underside, and hatch in about five days. When depositing an egg, the female settles on the upper edge of the leaf and curves the abdomen underneath the leaf, keeping her wings vibrating rapidly.

Larva

When newly hatched the larva is 1·5 mm long with a black head; the grey body is crossed by white transverse bands and has black spots bearing short bristles. When the larva is fully grown, the head is black and the body variable in colour. It may be any shade of green from pale to blackish; the dorsal, subdorsal and spiracular stripes may be dark green, whitish, or yellow. In all varieties the body bears black spots, each with a short pale bristle. There are only three pairs of prolegs.

The eggshell is not eaten. The larva is a semi-looper, and usually feeds at night. It is common in gardens, and large numbers can sometimes cause damage, especially to plants of the cabbage family and to geraniums.

Pupa

The pupa is slightly roughened, with a well-developed haustellum. It is black, with a little green shading on the wingcases and the ventral surface of the abdomen. It is enclosed in a thin, transparent cocoon spun among leaves, and the adult moth emerges in about two weeks.

NOCTUIDAE (CATOCALINAE) **Red Underwing**

Wingspan 70–90 mm

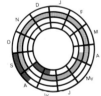

IMAGO
EGG
LARVA
PUPA

Distribution
England as far north as Yorkshire, and Wales. Commonest in the southern counties of England, but scarce in the south-west of England and western Wales.

Habitat
Woodland, parkland, and river valleys.

Life cycle
One generation a year. Over-winters as an egg.

Larval foodplants
Willows (*Salix* spp.) and poplars (*Populus* spp.).

Imago
The forewing is grey, slightly suffused with brown, and with dark grey zig-zag transverse lines. The reniform stigma is outlined in grey. The hindwing is red with a broad black marginal band and a narrower black wavy median line. The sexes are similar, but the antennae of the male are very shortly ciliate and those of the female sparsely ciliate for half their length.

Variation occurs commonly in the ground colour of both fore- and hindwings. In one extreme form – ab. *brunnescens* – the ground colour of the hindwings is brown.

The moth flies at night, visits over-ripe fruit and comes to sugar, but is seldom attracted to light. During the day it rests on tree trunks, fences, walls and telegraph poles, where the cryptic colouration of the forewings provides excellent camouflage.

Egg; width 1 mm

Larva in June; length 41 mm

Fully-grown larva; length 68 mm

Pupa; length 30 mm

Egg

The eggs are dome-shaped, strongly ribbed, and reticulated. They are whitish when laid, but soon become ochreous and are encircled by two purplish-brown bands. They are laid singly or in pairs, either on the bark or in a crevice of the bark of the foodplant, and overwinter, hatching in April.

Larva

When newly hatched the larva is 4 mm long; the head is pale brown and the body darker brown. By the time the larva is half grown, the dark brown has developed paler longitudinal stripes, and on the fifth abdominal segment there is now a prominent dorsal hump surrounded by a blackish-brown colouring. When the larva is fully grown the head is pale reddish-brown and very flattened,

and the body is pale grey-brown, faintly marked with darker lines, and still with the dorsal hump on the fifth abdominal segment. There are five pairs of prolegs and a fringe of short grey hairs below the spiracles.

The eggshell is not eaten. The larva feeds at night, and during the day rests stretched out along a twig or in a bark crevice. It is extremely difficult to detect.

Pupa

The pupa is reddish-brown, but this colour is completely concealed by a bluish-white bloom, which gives it a very mouldy appearance. It is contained in a coarse open-work cocoon of greyish-white silk spun between leaves or in a bark crevice. The adult moth emerges in three to four weeks.

NOCTUIDAE (CATOCALINAE) **Mother Shipton**

Wingspan 30–34 mm

IMAGO
EGG
LARVA
PUPA

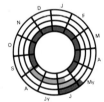

Distribution
England, Wales and Ireland, and also local populations in Scotland as far north as Ross-shire.

Habitat
Open woodland, downland, meadows, grassy hillsides, waste ground, grassy banks, and heathland.

Life cycle
One generation a year. Overwinters as a pupa.

Larval foodplants
Clover (*Trifolium* spp.), lucerne (*Medicago sativa*).

Imago
The forewing is dark brown, shaded with ochreous, and with a complicated pattern of whitish lines forming the witch-like profile of 'Mother Shipton'. The hindwing is dark brown with whitish-ochreous spots. The fringes of both wings are chequered brown and white. The sexes are similar, but the antennae of the male are more densely ciliate than those of the female.

Variation is common, both in the extent of the pale markings and in their shade – in some specimens this is quite yellow.

The moth flies by day and is very active in sunshine, taking short rapid flights. It is difficult to approach, and when resting between flights usually keeps the wings quivering.

Callistege mi (CLERCK)

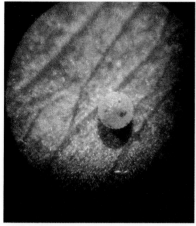

Egg; width 0·8 mm

Fully-grown larva; length 33 mm

Pupa; length 14 mm

Egg

The eggs are globular, ribbed, and reticulated. They are yellowish-green in colour, and are laid singly on leaves of the foodplant, hatching in about twelve days.

Larva

When newly hatched the larva is 2 mm long; the head is pale brown and the body ochreous. When the larva is fully grown its body is very slender, and its head and body are ochreous or pale yellow. There are narrow dark brown dorsal, subdorsal and lateral lines, a broad yellowish spiracular stripe, and three pairs of prolegs.

The eggshell is not eaten. The larva is a looper, and feeds either by day or night. If disturbed, it drops to the ground and rolls into a ring with its head touching the rear claspers.

Pupa

The pupa is reddish-brown, but this colour is covered by a thick blue-grey bloom. It is enclosed in a stout cocoon spun in low herbage.

NOCTUIDAE (OPHIDERINAE) **The Herald**

Wingspan 44–50 mm

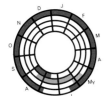

Distribution
Throughout the British Isles, but local in Scotland.

Habitat
Woodland, gardens, commons, marshy places, river valleys, and hedgerows.

Life cycle
One generation a year. Over-winters as an adult.

Larval foodplants
Willows and osier (*Salix spp.*), and poplars (*Populus spp.*).

Imago
The forewing is reddish-brown with ochreous transverse lines and a white basal spot. The orbicular stigma is white, and there are reddish-orange patches in the central and basal areas. The wingtip is hooked, and the outer margin crenate. The hindwing is reddish-brown. The sexes are similar, except that females are often larger, and their antennae are serrate while those of the males are pectinate.

Variation can occur in the shade of the ground colour, and in the size and brightness of the orange patches.

The moth flies at night, is attracted to light; in the autumn it feeds at ivy blossom and ripe black-berries, and in the spring at sallow blossom. It

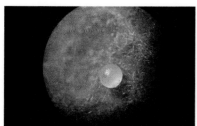

Egg; width 1 mm

Half-grown larva; length 17 mm

Fully-grown larva; length 40 mm

Pupa; length 20 mm

Cocoon

hibernates in outhouses, barns, old buildings or evergreens, and pairing takes place in spring.

Egg

The eggs are dome-shaped, finely ribbed, and reticulated, of a pale green colour. They are laid either singly or in groups of two or three on leaves of the foodplant, usually on the underside, and hatch in seven to ten days.

Larva

When newly hatched the larva is 2 mm long and its head and body are ochreous. By the time the larva is half grown, its head is pale yellowish-green and its body olive green with white subdorsal stripes edged below with darker green. When it is fully grown its body is long and slender, and its head and body are green, the latter appearing very velvety. There is a dark green dorsal line and a black-edged green subdorsal line. Five pairs of prolegs are present, the anal pair being widely spread.

The eggshell is partially eaten. The larva feeds mainly at night; when young it rests in the daytime on the underside of a foodplant leaf, but an older larva usually rests along a leaf stem high up on the foodplant.

Pupa

The pupa is black and dull, with a slightly roughened surface. It is contained in a cocoon of white silk concealed inside a rolled leaf, or between two leaves of the foodplant. The adult moth emerges in about three weeks.

NOCTUIDAE (OPHIDERINAE) **Small Purple-barred**

Wingspan 18–22 mm

IMAGO
EGG
LARVA
PUPA

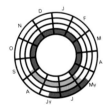

Distribution
Throughout the British Isles – commonest in southern districts of England, Wales and Ireland.

Habitat
Chalk downland, grassy banks, woodland rides, heathland and moorland.

Life cycle
One generation a year. Overwinters as a pupa.

Larval foodplants
The leaves and flowers of common milkwort (*Polygala vulgaris*). Also recorded on lousewort (*Pedicularis sylvatica*).

Imago
The forewing is olive brown with two rosy-purple transverse bands. The hindwing is greyish-olive, shaded darker grey towards the outer margin. The sexes are similar, but the antennae of the female are more shortly ciliate than those of the male.

Variation occurs in the ground colour of the forewing and the intensity of colour of the transverse band. In ab. *fusca* most of the rosy purple is missing, the forewing being dull brown.

The moth flies by day, and is active in sunshine, taking short rapid flights. Sometimes it will fly at dusk, and it is occasionally attracted to light.

Egg
The egg is rounded and covered with a triangular reticulation with short spines. It is white when laid, but within thirty-six hours two circular patterns of red blotches develop, and just before

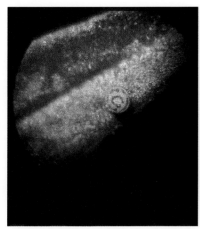

Egg; width 0·5 mm   Fully-grown larva; length 18 mm   Pupa; length 9 mm

hatching the whole egg is purplish-red. Eggs are laid singly or in groups of two or three on leaves of the foodplant, and hatch in about seven days.

Larva

When newly hatched the larva is 2 mm long, ochreous, and a looper. When it is fully grown its head and body are green with a whitish spiracular line and small black dots, each with a long fine bristle. There are three pairs of functional prolegs and one vestigial pair, and the larva is a semi-looper.

The eggshell is eaten. The larva feeds at night, and during the day rests along a stem of the foodplant.

Pupa

The pupa is cylindrical; the wingcases are greenish-brown and dull and the remainder of the body is dark reddish-brown and shiny, though the abdomen is paler brown ventrally. The cremaster points upwards. The pupa is enclosed in a dense cocoon of whitish silk among leaves or in litter on the surface of the ground.

NOCTUIDAE (HYPENINAE) **The Snout**

Wingspan 34–42 mm

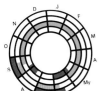

IMAGO
EGG
LARVA
PUPA

Distribution
Throughout the British Isles.

Habitat
Waste ground, gardens, ditches, hedgerows, and woodland wherever nettles grow.

Life cycle
Two generations a year, except in northern Britain, where there is only one and this produces adults in July and August. Overwinters as a young larva.

Larval foodplant
Common nettle (*Urtica dioica*).

Imago
The forewing is brown, patterned with various shades of darker brown, freckled with black, and with a few white dots. The hindwing is grey-brown, shaded darker towards the outer margin. The palpi are very long, and project forwards. The sexes are similar, but the antennae of the male are weakly ciliate while those of the female are simple. Individuals of the first generation are usually larger than those of the second.

Variation in the shade of the ground colour can occur.

The moth flies at night, becoming active at dusk, visits flowers, and is attracted to light. The English name refers to the long palpi.

Hypena proboscidalis (LINNAEUS)

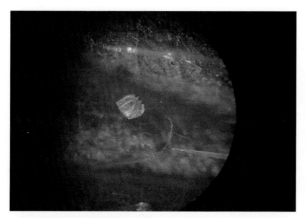

Egg; width 0·75 mm

Larva after hibernation; length 14 mm

Fully-grown larva; length 25 mm

Pupa; length 15 mm

Egg

The eggs are dome-shaped with a rather flattened top, strongly ribbed, and faintly reticulated. They are green in colour, becoming brown just before hatching. They are laid singly on nettle leaves and hatch in about eight days.

Larva

When newly hatched the larva is 2 mm long; the head is brown and the body ochreous with short pale hairs. When the larva is about half grown, its head is yellowish-green and its body green with faint white lines and spots. When it is fully grown its head is yellowish-green and its body green or yellowish-green, with yellow between the segments. There is a dark green dorsal line and a whitish spiracular line. The body bears scattered short brownish hairs, and there are four pairs of prolegs.

The eggshell is not eaten. The larva feeds at night, and during the day rests either underneath a nettle leaf, or between two leaves spun together. If disturbed, it falls from the plant and rolls into a knot. Larvae of the second generation begin hibernation towards the end of September or the beginning of October, among withered leaves or litter at the base of the foodplant, remaining dormant until the following spring.

Pupa

The pupa is dark reddish-brown with a darker brown dorsal line. It is smooth and shiny, and enclosed in a loose open-work cocoon spun among nettle leaves. The adult moth emerges in three to four weeks.

IDENTIFICATION PLATES
All specimens are shown life size

Abbreviations

Flight times
January–December: Ja, F, M, Ap, My, J, Jy, A, Sp, O, N, D

Distribution

T	throughout the British Isles
E	England
W	Wales
S	Scotland
I	Ireland (includes Northern Ireland and Eire)
s	south

w	west
e	east
n	north
c	central
loc.	local
v. loc.	very local
mig.	migrant
res.	resident
occ.	occasionally
fp.	foodplant (unless otherwise specified the part of the foodplant eaten by the larva is the leaves)

PLATE 1: *Hepialidae, Cossidae, Zygaenidae, Limacodidae, Sesiidae*

Hepialidae

1 **Ghost Moth** *Hepialus humuli* Linnaeus ♂
2 **Ghost Moth** *Hepialus humuli* Linnaeus ♀; J, Jy; T; grassy areas; fp. roots, incl. grasses, dock, burdock
3 **Orange Swift** *H. sylvina* Linn. ♂
4 **Orange Swift** *H. sylvina* Linn. ♀; Jy–Sp; E, W, S; rough ground, moorland; fp. roots, incl. bracken, dock, dandelion
5 **Gold Swift** *H. hecta* Linn. ♂
6 **Gold Swift** *H. hecta* Linn. ♀; J, Jy; T; woodland rides, commons; fp. bracken (roots & stems)
7 **Common Swift** *H. lupulinus* Linn. ♂
8 **Common Swift** *H. lupulinus* Linn. ♀; My–Jy; E, W, loc. in S, I; meadows, cultivated land; fp. roots, incl. grasses, dandelion
9 **Map-winged Swift** *H. fusconebulosa* De Geer ♂; My–Jy; loc. T; hillsides, wood edges; fp. bracken (roots & stems)

Cossidae (Zeuzerinae)

10 **Reed Leopard** *Phragmataecia castaneae* Hübner ♂
11 **Reed Leopard** *Phragmataecia castaneae* Hübner ♀; J, Jy; v. loc. East Anglia, Dorset; reed-beds; fp. common reed (inside stems)
13 **Leopard Moth** *Zeuzera pyrina* Linn.; J–A; c&sE, eW; woodland, orchards; fp. trees incl. ash, lilac, fruit trees (inside stems & branches)

Cossidae (Cossinae)

12 **Goat Moth** *Cossus cossus* Linn.; J. Jy; E, W, cS, sI; vicinity of trees; fp. trees incl. oak, willow (inside solid wood)

Zygaenidae (Procridinae)

14 **Scarce Forester** *Adscita globulariae* Hb.; J, Jy; v. loc. sE; chalk downs; fp. common & greater knapweeds
15 **The Forester** *A. statices* Linn.; J, Jy; loc. T; chalk downs, damp meadows; fp. sorrels
17 **Cistus Forester** *A. geryon* Hb.; J, Jy; s&cE, nW; chalk downs; fp. common rock-rose

Zygaenidae (Zygaeninae)

16 **Six-spot Burnet** *Zygaena filipendulae* Dupont; J–A; E, W, I, coastal S; meadows, downs, woodland rides; fp. bird's-foot trefoil
18 **Scotch Burnet** *Z. exulans* White; J, Jy; v. loc. Aberdeenshire; mountains above 600 m; fp. crowberry
19 **Narrow-bordered Five-spot Burnet** *Z. lonicerae* Tutt; J, Jy; E except sw, Skye, nI, seW; downland, rough ground; fp. trefoils, clovers, vetches
20 **Slender Scotch Burnet** *Z. loti* Rowland-Brown; J, Jy; Mull, Ulva; grassy coastal slopes; fp. bird's-foot trefoil
21 **New Forest Burnet** *Z. viciae* Tremewan; Jy; v. loc. Argyll; grassy coastal slopes; fp. bird's-foot trefoil, meadow vetchling
22 **Five-spot Burnet** *Z. trifolii decreta* Verity; J–A; s&wE, W, Isle of Man; damp meadows, marshes; fp. greater bird's-foot trefoil
23 **Five-spot Burnet** *Z. trifolii palustrella* Ver.; My, J; se&csE; chalk downs; fp. bird's-foot trefoil
24 **Transparent Burnet** *Z. purpuralis* Trem.; J, Jy; Hebrides, Argyll, wI; grassy slopes; fp. thyme

Limacodidae

25 **The Festoon** *Apoda limacodes* Hufnagel ♂
31 **The Festoon** *Apoda limacodes* Hufnagel ♀; J, Jy; s&seE; woodland; fp. oak, beech
26 **The Triangle** *Heterogenea asella* Denis & Schiffermüller ♂
32 **The Triangle** *Heterogenea asella* Denis & Schiffermüller ♀; J, Jy; v. loc. s&seE; woodland; fp. beech, oak

Sesiidae (Sesiinae)

27 **Hornet Moth** *Sesia apiformis* Clerck ♂
28 **Hornet Moth** *Sesia apiformis* Clerck ♀; J, Jy; se&csE, v. loc. sI; vicinity of poplars; fp. poplars (inside lower trunks)
33 **Lunar Hornet Moth** *S. bembeciformis* Hb. ♂
34 **Lunar Hornet Moth** *S. bembeciformis* Hb. ♀; Jy; T; damp woodland, marshy areas; fp. sallows (inside trunks)

Sesiidae (Paranthreninae)

29 **Currant Clearwing** *Synanthedon tipuliformis* Cl.; J, Jy; E, W, loc. S & I; gardens; fp. currants (inside stems)
30 **White-barred Clearwing** *S. spheciformis* D. & S.; My–Jy; s&cE to Yorks., n&sW; marshy areas, heathland; fp. birch, alder (inside trunks & stumps)
35 **Welsh Clearwing** *S. scoliaeformis* Borkhausen; J, Jy; v. loc. Perthshire, swI; birch woods; fp. birch (inner bark)
36 **Yellow-legged Clearwing** *S. vespiformis* Linn. ♂
37 **Yellow-legged Clearwing** *S. vespiformis* Linn. ♀; My–A; s&cE to Yorks.; woodland; fp. oak (beneath bark)

PLATE 2: *Sesiidae, Lasiocampidae*

Sesiidae (Paranthreninae)

1 **Sallow Clearwing** *Synanthedon flaviventris* Staudinger; J, Jy; cs&seE; damp woodland & heathland; fp. sallows (inside stems)
2 **Orange-tailed Clearwing** *S. anthraciniformis* Esper; My–Jy; sE; downland, wood edges; fp. wayfaring tree (inside stems)
3 **Red-belted Clearwing** *S. myopaeformis* Borkhausen; J, Jy; sE; gardens, orchards; fp. fruit trees (under bark)
4 **Red-tipped Clearwing** *S. formicaeformis* Esp.; J–A; E, sW, loc. in I; marshy places, osier beds; fp. sallows (inside stems)
5 **Large Red-belted Clearwing** *S. culiciformis* Linnaeus; My, J; E, W, S; open woodland; fp. birch (under bark of stumps)

6 **Six-belted Clearwing** *Bembecia scopigera* Scopoli; J–A; sE, sW; chalk downs, sea-cliffs; fp. bird's-foot trefoil (roots)
7 **Thrift Clearwing** *B. muscaeformis* Esp.; J, Jy; wE, W, eS, sI, Isle of Man; sea-cliffs; fp. thrift (crowns & roots)
8 **Fiery Clearwing** *B. chrysidiformis* Esp.; J, Jy; v. loc. Kent; sea-cliffs; fp. dock, sorrel (crowns & roots)

Lasiocampidae

9 **Pale Eggar** *Trichiura crataegi* Linn. ♂
10 **Pale Eggar** *Trichiura crataegi* Linn. ♀; A, Sp, Jy in S; E, W, S, loc. in I; woodland, hedgerows; fp. trees, shrubs, incl. Hawthorn, blackthorn, oak
11 **The Lackey** *Malacosoma neustria* Linn. ♂
12 **The Lackey** *Malacosoma neustria* Linn. ♀; Jy, A; W, I, sE, loc. in nE; woodland, hedgerows. fp. trees, shrubs incl. hawthorn, birch, sallow
13 **December Moth** *Poecilocampa populi* Linn.; O–D; T; woodland, hedgerows; fp. trees incl. oak, birch

14 **Small Eggar** *Eriogaster lanestris* Linn.; F, M; loc. E; hedgerows; fp. hawthorn, blackthorn
15 **Ground Lackey** *Malacosoma castrensis* Linn. ♂
16 **Ground Lackey** *Malacosoma castrensis* Linn. ♀; Jy, A; loc. seE; salt-marshes; fp. sea plantain, sea lavender
17 **Grass Eggar** *Lasiocampa trifolii* Denis & Schiffermüller ♂
18 **Grass Eggar** *Lasiocampa trifolii* Denis & Schiffermüller ♀; A, Sp; v. loc. s&nwE, W; sand hills, sea-cliffs; fp. various, incl. grasses, creeping willow
19 **Oak Eggar** *L. quercus* Linn. ♂
20 **Oak Eggar** *L. quercus* Linn. ♀; Jy, A; E northwards to Lancs; woodland, downland; fp. various incl. hawthorn, bramble, sallow
21 **Northern Eggar** *L. quercus callunae* Palmer. ♂
22 **Northern Eggar** *L. quercus callunae* Palmer ♀; My, J; sw, c&nE, sI; heathland, moorland; fp. heather, bilberry

PLATE 3: *Lasiocampidae,*
Saturniidae,
Endromidae

Lasiocampidae

1 **Fox Moth** *Macrothylacia rubi*
Linnaeus ♂

2 **Fox Moth** *Macrothylacia rubi*
Linnaeus ♀; My–Jy; T; downland,
heathland, fp. various incl. heather,
bramble

3 **The Drinker** *Philudoria potatoria*
Linn. ♂

4 **The Drinker** *Philudoria potatoria*
Linn. ♀; Jy, A; E, W, I, wS; damp
woodland & moorland; fp. grasses &
reeds

5 **The Lappet** *Gastropacha quercifolia*
Linn.; J–A; sE, W; hedgerows, open
woodland; fp. hawthorn,
blackthorn, sallow

6 **Small Lappet** *Phyllodesma ilicifolia*
Linn.; Ap, My; v. loc. swE;
moorland; fp. bilberry

Saturniidae

7 **Emperor Moth** *Pavonia pavonia* Linn.
♂

8 **Emperor Moth** *Pavonia pavonia* Linn.
♀; Ap, My; T; heathland, commons;
fp. various incl. heather, bramble

Endromidae

9 **Kentish Glory** *Endromis versicolora*
Linn. ♂

10 **Kentish Glory** *Endromis versicolora*
Linn. ♀; M, Ap; v. loc. in S;
moorland, open woodland; fp. birch

PLATE 4: *Drepanidae, Thyatiridae, Geometridae*

Drepanidae

1 **Scalloped Hook-tip** *Falcaria lacertinaria* Linnaeus; My, J, Jy–Sp (E, W, I), My, J (S); T; Woodland, heathland. fp. birch

2 **Oak Hook-tip** *Drepana binaria* Hufnagel; My, J, A; E, W; woodland, parks; fp. oak

3 **Barred Hook-tip** *D. cultraria* Fabricius; My, J, A, Sp; sE; beechwoods; fp. beech

4 **Pebble Hook-tip** *D. falcataria* Linn.; My, J, A, Sp (E, W, I), My, J (S); T; woodland, heathland, fp. birch

5 **Scarce Hook-tip** *Sabra harpagula* Esper; J, Jy; v. loc. W, Glos,; woodland, fp. small-leaved lime

6 **Chinese Character** *Cilix glaucata* Scopoli; My, J, Jy, A; E, W, I, sS; hedgerows, bushy areas; fp. hawthorn, blackthorn

Thyatiridae

7 **Peach Blossom** *Thyatira batis* Linn.; My–Jy, occ. A, Sp in sE; T; woodland; fp. bramble

8 **Buff Arches** *Habrosyne pyritoides* Hufn.; J–A; E, W, I; woodland; fp. bramble

9 **Satin Lutestring** *Tetheella fluctuosa* Hübner; J–A; v. loc. se, c&nwE, W, S, I; woodland; fp. birch

10 **Poplar Lutestring** *Tethea or* Denis & Schiffermüller; My–A; T; woodland, parkland; fp. aspen, poplar

11 **Common Lutestring** *Ochropacha duplaris* Linn.; J–A; T; woodland; fp. birch

12 **Oak Lutestring** *Cymatophorima diluta* Reisser; A, Sp; E, W, sS; woodland; fp. oak

13 **Figure of Eighty** *Tethea ocularis* Hb.; My–Jy; E, eW; woodland, parks; fp. poplar, aspen

14 **Yellow Horned** *Achlya flavicornis* Tutt; M, Ap; E, W, S; woodland, heathland; fp. birch

15 **Frosted Green** *Polyploca ridens* Fabr.

16 **Frosted Green** *Polyploca ridens* Fabr. (melanic); Ap, My; sE, W, loc. c&nE; woodland; fp. oak

Geometridae (Oenochrominae)

17 **March Moth** *Alsophila aescularia* D. & S. ♂

18 **March Moth** *Alsophila aescularia* D. & S. ♀; M, Ap; T; woodland, hedgerows; fp. trees, shrubs incl. oak, hazel, hawthorn

Geometridae (Archiearinae)

19 **Orange Underwing** *Archiearis parthenias* Linn. ♂

20 **Orange Underwing** *Archiearis parthenias* Linn. ♀; M, Ap; E, W, S; woodland, heathland; fp. birch

21 **Light Orange Underwing** *A. notha* Hb. ♂

22 **Light Orange Underwing** *A. notha* Hb. ♀; M, Ap; v. loc. sE; woodland; fp. aspen

Geometridae (Geometrinae)

23 **Rest Harrow** *Aplasta ononaria* Fuessly; J, Jy; occ. A, Sp; res. Kent, mig, sE; coastal sand hills; fp. common rest harrow

24 **Large Emerald** *Geometra papilionaria* Linn.; J–A; T; woodland, heathland; fp. birch, hazel

25 **Grass Emerald** *Pseudoterpna pruinata* Walker; J–A; E, W, I, sS; heathland, commons; fp. petty whin, gorse

26 **Blotched Emerald** *Comibaena bajularia* D. & S.; J, Jy; s, c&nE, eW; woodland; fp. oak

.27 **Essex Emerald** *Thetidia smaragdaria* Prout; J, Jy; v. loc. Essex, Kent; salt-marshes; fp. sea-wormwood

28 **Small Grass Emerald** *Chlorissa viridata* Linn.; J, Jy; v. loc. s, sw, w&nE, East Anglia; damp heathland; fp. heather, creeping willow, birch

29 **Little Emerald** *Jodis lactearia* Linn.; My, J; E, W, I, wS; woodland; fp. various, incl. birch, hawthorn

30 **Common Emerald** *Hemithea aestivaria* Hb.; J, Jy; E, W, I, Isle of Man; hedgerows, bushy areas; fp. trees & shrubs incl. oak, hawthorn

31 **Small Emerald** *Hemistola chrysoprasaria* Esp.; J–A; sE, W, loc. c&nE; chalk downs, hedgerows; fp. traveller's-joy

Geometridae (Sterrhinae)

32 **Dingy Mocha** *Cyclophora pendularia* Clerck; My, J, Jy, A; v. loc. s Dorset, w Hants; damp heathland; fp. sallow

33 **The Mocha** *C. annulata* Schulze; My, J, Jy, A; sE, W; woodland; fp. maple

34 **Birch Mocha** *C. albipunctata* Hufn.; My, J, A; E, W, I, c&nS; woodland, heathland; fp. birch

35 **False Mocha** *C. porata* Linn.; My, J, A, Sp; s&cE, W; woodland; fp. oak

36 **Blair's Mocha** *C. puppillaria* Hb.; A–O; sE (mig); fp. evergreen oak

37 **Maiden's Blush** *C. punctaria* Linn. (spring)

38 **Maiden's Blush** *C. punctaria* Linn. (summer); My, J, A, Sp; E, W, sS, loc.in I; woodland; fp. oak, birch

39 **Clay Triple-lines** *C. linearia* Hb.; My–Jy, occ. A–O; s&cE, sW, loc. in I; beechwoods; fp. beech

40 **Blood-vein** *Timandra griseata* Petersen; My–Jy, A, Sp; E, W, sS, swI; waste ground, hedgerows; fp. dock, sorrel, knotgrass

41 **Sub-angled Wave** *Scopula nigropunctata* Hufn.; Jy, A; v. loc. Kent; hedgerows; fp. uncertain (in captivity – traveller's-joy, dandelion)

42 **Lace Border** *S. ornata* Scop.; My, J, Jy–Sp; seE, v. loc. in sE; chalk downs; fp. thyme, marjoram

43 **Mullein Wave** *S. marginepunctata* Goeze; J, Jy, A, Sp; coastal s, w&nE, W, wS, I, Isle of Man; rough ground; fp. yarrow, plantain, mugwort

44 **Small Blood-vein** *S. imitaria* Hb.; Jy, A; E, W, sI; hedgerows, bushy areas; fp. privet

45 **Rosy Wave** *S. emutaria* Hb.; J, Jy; s&eE, W; bogs, coastal marshes; fp. uncertain (in captivity – dandelion, knotgrass)

PLATE 5: *Geometridae*

Geometridae (Sterrhinae)

1 **Tawny Wave** *Scopula rubiginata* Hufnagel; J, Jy, A, Sp; res. East Anglia, mig. s&eE; coastal sand hills; fp. unrecorded (in captivity – dandelion)

2 **Lesser Cream Wave** *S. immutata* Linnaeus; J–A; loc. E, W, I; marshes, damp woodland; fp. meadowsweet, common valerian

3 **Cream Wave** *S. floslactata* Haworth; My, J; T; woodland; fp. dock, bedstraws

4 **Smoky Wave** *S. ternata* Schrank; J, Jy; W, c&nE, S, loc. swE; heathland, mosses; fp. bilberry, heather

5 **Bright Wave** *Idaea ochrata* Prout; J–A; v. loc. e&seE; coastal sand hills; fp. unrecorded (in captivity – knotgrass)

6 **Purple-bordered Gold** *I. muricata* Hufn.

7 **Purple-bordered Gold** *I. muricata* f. *totarubra* Lambillion; J, Jy; loc. E, W, v. loc. I; damp heathland, fens; fp. cinquefoils

8 **Least Carpet** *I. vulpinaria* Lempke; Jy, A; e&seE; hedgerows, chalk downs; fp. traveller's-joy, ivy

9 **Dotted Border Wave** *I. sylvestraria* Hübner; J–A; s&cE; heathland; fp. unrecorded (in captivity – dandelion)

10 **Small Fan-footed Wave** *I. biselata* Hufn.; J–A; T; woodland, hedgerows; fp. unrecorded (in captivity – dandelion, bramble)

11 **Silky Wave** *I. dilutaria* Hb.; Jy; loc. Avon, Gt Orme; limestone downs; fp. common rock-rose (withered leaves)

12 **Dwarf Cream Wave** *I. fuscovenosa* Goeze; J, Jy; E, I; hedgerows; fp. unrecorded (in captivity – dandelion, bramble)

13 **Small Dusty Wave** *I. seriata* Schr.; J, Jy, A, Sp (Jy, A in n); E, W, eS; hedgerows, waste ground; fp. ivy

14 **Single-dotted Wave** *I. dimidiata* Hufn.; J–A; E, W, I, swS; damp woodland, marshes; fp. cow parsley, burnet saxifrage

15 **Satin Wave** *I. subsericeata* Haw.; J, Jy, A, Sp; T; grassy areas, downland; fp. unrecorded (in captivity – dandelion, knotgrass)

16 **Weaver's Wave** *I. contiguaria* Müller; J, Jy; v. loc. nwW; mountain moorland; fp. heather, crowberry

17 **Treble Brown Spot** *I. trigeminata* Haw.; J, Jy, occ. Jy, A; sE, sW; hedgerows, waste ground; fp. ivy, knotgrass

18 **Small Scallop** *I. emarginata* Linn.♂

19 **Small Scallop** *I. emarginata* Linn.♀; J–A; E, W; damp woodland, fens; fp. bedstraws

20 **Portland Ribbon Wave** *I. degeneraria* Hb.; J, Jy; loc. Portland (Dorset); grassy sea-cliffs; fp. unrecorded (in captivity – dandelion)

21 **The Vestal** *Rhodometra sacraria* Linn.; My–O; mig. sE; fp. unrecorded (in captivity – dock, knotgrass)

22 **Plain Wave** *Idaea straminata* Borkhausen; Jy; loc. T; woodland, heathland; fp. unrecorded (in captivity – knotgrass)

23 **Riband Wave** *I. aversata* Linn.

24 **Riband Wave** *I. aversata* ab. *remutata* Linn.; J–A, also Sp in s; T; hedgerows, waste ground; fp. bedstraw, chickweed

Geometridae (Larentiinae)

25 **Oblique Striped** *Phibalapteryx virgata* Hufn.; My, J, A; loc. E, W; coastal sand hills, chalk downs; fp. lady's bedstraw

26 **Oblique Carpet** *Orthonama vittata* Borkh.; My, J, A, Sp; T; marshy areas, fens; fp. bedstraws

27 **The Gem** *O. obstipata* Fabricius; My–N; mig. E, I; fp. unrecorded (in captivity – groundsel)

28 **Flame Carpet** *Xanthorhoe designata* Hufn.; My, J, A; T; damp woodland, hedgerows; fp. unrecorded (in captivity – crucifers)

29 **Balsam Carpet** *X. biriviata* Borkh. (spring)

30 **Balsam Carpet** *X. biriviata* Borkh. (summer); My, J, Jy–Sp; loc. seE, East Anglia; water meadows; fp. orange balsam

31 **Red Carpet** *X. munitata* Hb.; J–A; c&nE, nW, S, nI; mountain moorland; fp. lady's mantle

32 **Red Twin-spot Carpet** *X. spadicearia* Denis & Schiffermüller; My, J, Jy, A; T; hedgerows, bushy areas; fp. bedstraws

33 **Dark-barred Twin-spot Carpet** *X. ferrugata* Clerck; My, J, Jy, A; T; hedgerows, bushy areas; fp. unrecorded (in captivity – dandelion, dock)

34 **Large Twin-spot Carpet** *X. quadrifasiata* Cl.; J–A; E to Yorks; seW; woodland, hedgerows; fp. bedstraws

35 **Silver-ground Carpet** *X. montanata* D.& S.; My–Jy; T; downland, grassy areas; fp. bedstraws

36 **Garden Carpet** *X. fluctuata* Linn.; My–O; T; gardens, hedgerows; fp. crucifers

37 **Spanish Carpet** *Scotopteryx peribolata* Hb.; A, Sp; Channel Islands; sea-cliffs; fp. broom

38 **Chalk Carpet** *S. bipunctaria* Prout; Jy, A; E, W; chalk downs, limestone hills; fp. trefoils, clovers

39 **Shaded Broad-bar** *S. chenopodiata* Linn.; Jy, A; T; downland, waste ground; fp. clovers, vetches

40 **Ruddy Carpet** *Catarhoe rubidata* D. & S.; J, Jy; loc. sE, sW; downland, hedgerows; fp. bedstraws

41 **Lead Belle** *Scotopteryx mucronata* Heydemann; My, J; sw&nE, W, S, I, Isle of Man; heathland; fp. gorse, broom

42 **July Belle** *S. luridata* Fabr.; J–A; T; heathland, downland; fp. gorse, petty whin

43 **Royal Mantle** *Catarhoe cuculata* Hufn.; J, Jy; sE, East Anglia, Perthshire, the Burren; downland, hedgerows, sea-cliffs; fp. bedstraws

44 **Small Argent and Sable** *Epirrhoe tristata* Linn.; My–A; sw, c&nE, S, I; mountain moorland, limestone hills; fp. heath bedstraw

45 **Common Carpet** *E. alternata* Müll.; My, J, A, Sp; T; hedgerows, waste ground; fp. bedstraws

46 **Galium Carpet** *E. galiata* D. & S.; My–A; T; chalk downs, sea-cliffs, grassy areas; fp. bedstraws

47 **Wood Carpet** *E. rivata* Hb.; J–A; s&cE&W, loc. in nE & sS; wood edges, downland; fp. bedstraws

48 **Yellow Shell** *Camptogramma bilineata* Linn.; J–A; T; hedgerows, grassy areas; fp. chickweed, dock

49 **Yellow-ringed Carpet** *Entephria flavicinctata* Hb.; Jy, A (E) My, A (S,I); Yorks., nI, c&wS; rocky ravines; fp. saxifrages, English stonecrop

50 **Grey Mountain Carpet** *E. caesiata* D. & S.; J–A; c&nE, W, S, I, Isle of Man; mountains, moorlands; fp. heather, bilberry

51 **The Mallow** *Larentia clavaria* Haw.; Sp, O; E, W, I, sS; waste ground, roadsides; fp. common mallow

52 **Shoulder Stripe** *Anticlea badiata* D. & S.; M–My; T; hedgerows, bushy areas; fp. wild rose

53 **The Streamer** *A. derivata* D. & S.; Ap, My; T; hedgerows, bushy areas; fp. wild rose

54 **Beautiful Carpet** *Mesoleuca albicillata* Linn.; J, Jy; E, W, I, s&wS; woodland; fp. bramble, raspberry

55 **Dark Spinach** *Pelurga comitata* Linn.; Jy, A; E, W, I, sS; waste ground; fp. goosefoot, orache

56 **Purple Bar** *Cosmorhoe ocellata* Linn.; My–Jy, A, Sp; T; woodland, downland; fp. bedstraws

57 **Striped Twin-spot Carpet** *Nebula salicata* Curtis; My-Jy, A, Sp; sw&nE, W, S, I, Isle of Man; moorland, woodland; fp. bedstraws

58 **Devon Carpet** *Lamproteryx otregiata* Metcalfe; My, J, A, Sp; cs&swE, sW; damp woodland; fp. common marsh bedstraw

59 **Water Carpet** *L. suffumata* D. & S.

60 **Water Carpet** *L. suffumata* ab. *piceata* Stephens; Ap, My; T; hedgerows, bushy areas; fp. bedstraws

61 **The Chevron** *Eulithis testata* Linn.

62 **The Chevron** *Eulithis testata* Linn.; Jy–Sp; T; heathland, moorland, open woodland; fp. creeping willow, birch

PLATE 6: *Geometridae*

Geometridae (Larentiinae)

1 **The Phoenix** *Eulithis prunata* Linnaeus; Jy, A; T; gardens; fp. currants, gooseberry

2 **The Spinach** *E. mellinata* Fabricius; J–A; E, W, v. loc. in S&I; gardens; fp. currants

3 **Northern Spinach** *E. populata* Linn.; Jy, A; sw,c&nE, W, S, I, Isle of Man; moorland; fp. bilberry

4 **Barred Straw** *E. pyraliata* Denis & Schiffermüller; J–A; T; downland, bushy areas; fp. bedstraws

5 **Small Phoenix** *Ecliptopera silaceata* D. & S.; My, J also Jy, A in sE; T (except Isle of Man); woodland, waste ground; fp. willowherbs

6 **Red-green Carpet** *Chloroclysta siterata* Hufnagel; Sp, O, Ap, My; (hibernates); T; woodland; fp. oak, rowan

7 **Autumn Green Carpet** *C. miata* Linn.; Sp, O, M, Ap; (hibernates); T; woodland; fp. sallow, oak

8 **Dark Marbled Carpet** *C. citrata* Linn.

9 **Dark Marbled Carpet** *C. citrata* Linn.; Jy, A; T; woodland, moorland; fp. sallow, bilberry, birch

10 **Arran Carpet** *C. concinnata* Stephens; Jy, A; Arran, Kintyre, South Uist; mountain moorland; fp. heather

11 **Common Marbled Carpet** *C. truncata* Hufn.

12 **Common Marbled Carpet** *C. truncata* Hufn.

13 **Common Marbled Carpet** *C. truncata* Hufn.; My–N; T; woodland, hedgerows, waste ground; fp. various incl. birch, bramble

14 **Grey Pine Carpet** *Thera obeliscata* Hübner

15 **Grey Pine Carpet** *Thera obeliscata* Hübner; My–Jy, Sp, O; T; pinewoods; fp. conifers

16 **Barred Yellow** *Cidaria fulvata* Forster; J, Jy; T; woodland, bushy areas; fp. wild rose

17 **Blue-bordered Carpet** *Plemyria rubiginata* D. & S.; J–A; T; woodland, marshy areas; fp. alder, blackthorn

18 **Pine Carpet** *Thera firmata* Hb.; Jy–O; T; pinewoods; fp. pines

19 **Spruce Carpet** *T. britannica* Turner; My–Jy, Sp–O; T; spruce plantations; fp. spruces

20 **Chestnut-coloured Carpet** *T. cognata* Thunberg; Jy, A; W, nE, c&nS, wI; chalk downs, limestone hills; fp. juniper

21 **Juniper Carpet** *T. juniperata* Linn.; O, N; v. loc. s&nE, W, S, the Burren; chalk downs, limestone hills; fp. juniper

22 **Netted Carpet** *Eustroma reticulatum* D. & S.; Jy, A; v. loc. Cumbria, wW; damp woodland; fp. touch-me-not

23 **Broken-barred Carpet** *Electrophaes corylata* Thunb.; My, J; T; woodland, bushy areas; fp. oak, hawthorn, birch

24 **Beech-green Carpet** *Colostygia olivata* D. & S.; Jy, A; nE, nW, S, loc. in sE & wI; woodland, hedgerows; fp. bedstraws

25 **Mottled Grey** *C. multistrigaria* Haworth; M, Ap; E, W, S, nI; downland, heathland, woodland; fp. bedstraws

26 **Green Carpet** *C. pectinataria* Knoch; My–A; T; hedgerows, woodland; fp. bedstraws

27 **May Highflyer** *Hydriomena impluviata* D. & S.; My–Jy; T; vicinity of alders; fp. alder

28 **July Highflyer** *H. furcata* Thunb.

29 **July Highflyer** *H. furcata* Thunb.; Jy, A; T; woodland, moorland, hedgerows; fp. sallows, hazel, heather

30 **Ruddy Highflyer** *H. ruberata* Freyer

31 **Ruddy Highflyer** *H. ruberata* Freyer; My, J; nE, nW, S. loc. in swE, sW, n&wI; woodland, heathland; fp. sallows

32 **Pretty Chalk Carpet** *Melanthia procellata* D. & S.; J–A; s&cE, W; hedgerows, bushy areas; fp. traveller's-joy

33 **Slender-striped Rufous** *Coenocalpe lapidata* Hb.; Sp; loc. c&nS, nI; moorland, rough grassy hillsides; fp. unrecorded (in captivity – dandelion)

34 **Small Waved Umber** *Horisme vitalbata* D. & S.; My, J, A; s&eE, sW; hedgerows, bushy areas; fp. traveller's-joy

35 **The Fern** *H. tersata* D. & S.; J–A; sE, sW; hedgerows, bushy areas; fp. traveller's-joy

36 **Barberry Carpet** *Pareulype berberata* D. & S.; My, J, A; v. loc. Suffolk; hedgerows; fp. barberry

37 **White-banded Carpet** *Spargania luctuata* D. & S.; My, J, Jy, A; seE; woodland; fp. rosebay willowherb

38 **Scallop Shell** *Rheumaptera undulata* Linn.; J, Jy; E, W, I, sS; woodland, marshy areas; fp. sallow, bilberry, aspen

39 **Argent and Sable** *R. hastata* Linn.; My–Jy; E, W, c&w&nS, I; woodland, wet moorland; fp. birch, bog myrtle

40 **Scarce Tissue** *R. cervinalis* Scopoli; Ap–J; E, W; hedgerows, bushy areas; fp. barberry

41 **The Tissue** *Triphosa dubitata* Linn.; A, Sp, Ap, My; (hibernates); E, W, I; chalk downs, bushy areas; fp. buckthorn, alder buckthorn

42 **Brown Scallop** *Philereme vetulata* D. & S.; Jy; sE except sw, c&nE, sW; chalk downs, wood edges; fp. buckthorn

43 **Cloaked Carpet** *Euphyia biangulata* Haw.; Jy; v. loc. sE, sW, I; hedgerows, wood edges; fp. chickweeds

44 **Dark Umber** *Philereme transversata* Lempke; Jy; E, sW, wI; chalk downs, hedgerows; fp. buckthorn

45 **Sharp-angled Carpet** *Euphyia unangulata* Haw.; J–A; sE, W, I; hedgerows, woodland; fp. chickweeds

46 **November Moth** *Epirrita dilutata* D. & S.

47 **November Moth** *Epirrita dilutata* D. & S. (melanic); Sp–N; T; woodland; fp. trees & shrubs incl. oak, hawthorn

48 **Pale November Moth** *E. christyi* Allen; Sp–N; E, W, I, sS; woodland; fp. trees & shrubs incl. oak, hawthorn

49 **Autumnal Moth** *E. autumnata* Borkhausen; Sp, O; T; woodland, heathland; fp. birch, alder

50 **Small Autumnal Moth** *E. filigrammaria* Herrich-Schäffer; A, Sp; nE, c&nW, S, I, Isle of Man; moorland, mountainsides; fp. heather, bilberry

51 **Winter Moth** *Operophtera brumata* Linn. ♂

52 **Winter Moth** *Operophtera brumata* Linn. ♀; N–Ja; T; woodland, gardens, hedgerows; fp. most deciduous trees & shrubs

53 **Northern Winter Moth** *O. fagata* Scharfenberg ♂

54 **Northern Winter Moth** *O. fagata* Scharfenberg ♀; O–D; E (except sw), nW, S; woodland, heathland, orchards; fp. birch, fruit trees

PLATE 7: *Geometridae*

Geometridae (Larentiinae)

1 **Barred Carpet** *Perizoma taeniata* Stephens; J–A; loc. sw, c&nE, nW, S, I; damp woodland; fp. mosses

2 **The Rivulet** *P. affinitata* Steph.; My–Jy; E, W, S, nI; woodland, roadsides; fp. red campion (seeds)

3 **Small Rivulet** *P. alchemillata* Linnaeus; J–A; T; woodland, waste ground; fp. hemp-nettle (flowers & seeds)

4 **Barred Rivulet** *P. bifaciata* Haworth; Jy, A; E, W, sS, I; downland, waste ground; fp. red bartsia (seeds)

5 **Heath Rivulet** *P. minorata* Steph.; Jy, A; v. loc. nE, the Burren, loc. S; moorland, grassy uplands; fp. eyebright (seeds)

6 **Pretty Pinion** *P. blandiata* Denis & Schiffermüller; J, Jy; S, n&wI, v. loc. Cumbria, sW; moorland, grassy hillsides; fp. eyebright (flowers & seeds)

7 **Grass Rivulet** *P. albulata* D. & S.; My–Jy; T; downland, damp meadows; fp. yellow rattle (seeds)

8 **Sandy Carpet** *P. flavofasciata* Thunberg; J, Jy; E, W, S, nI; downland, roadsides; fp. campions (seeds)

9 **Twin-spot Carpet** *P. didymata* Linn.; J–A; T; woodland, roadsides, moorland; fp. grasses, willowherb, bilberry

10 **Marsh Carpet** *P. sagittata* Fabricius; J, Jy; v. loc. eE; fens, marshy areas; fp. common meadow-rue (seeds)

11 **Slender Pug** *Eupithecia tenuiata* Hübner; J, Jy; T; damp woodland, marshy areas; fp. sallows (catkins)

12 **Maple Pug** *E. inturbata* Hb.; Jy, A; E, W; woodland, downland; fp. field maple (flowers)

13 **Haworth's Pug** *E. haworthiata* Doubleday; J, Jy; E, W, I; downland, hedgerows; fp. traveller's-joy (in buds)

14 **Lead-coloured Pug** *E. plumbeolata* Haw.; My, J; E, W, wI; woodland; fp. common cow-wheat (flowers)

15 **Toadflax Pug** *E. linariata* D. & S.; Jy, A; E, W, loc. in S; waste ground, roadsides; fp. common toadflax (flowers & seeds)

16 **Foxglove Pug** *E. pulchellata* Steph; My, J; T; woodland rides, moorland, commons; fp. foxglove (stamens)

17 **Marbled Pug** *E. irriguata* Hb.; Ap, My; v. loc. sE; woodland; fp. oak

18 **Mottled Pug** *E. exiguata* Hb.; My, J; E, W, I, loc. S; woodland, hedgerows; fp. hawthorn, blackthorn, sycamore

19 **Pinion-spotted Pug** *E. insigniata* Hb.; My, J; loc. c&sE; hedgerows, bushy areas; fp. hawthorn

20 **Valerian Pug** *E. valerianata* Hb.; J, Jy; E, W, S, wI; fens, marshy areas; fp. common valerian (flowers & seeds)

21 **Marsh Pug** *E. pygmaeata* Hb.; My, J; v. loc. e, c&nE, W, S, w&nI, Isle of Man; marshy areas, waste ground; fp. field mouse-ear (flowers & seeds)

22 **Netted Pug** *E. venosata* Fabr.; My, J; E, W, neS, wI, Isle of Man, chalk & limestone areas, sea-cliffs; fp. bladder- & sea campion (seeds)

23 **Pauper Pug** *E. egenaria* Herrich-Schäffer; My, J; v. loc. Norfolk, Wye Valley; woodland; fp. limes (flowers)

24 **Lime-speck Pug** *E. centaureata* D. & S.; My–O; T; downland, waste ground; fp. various incl. yarrow, knapweed (flowers)

25 **Freyer's Pug** *E. intricata* Freyer; My, J; s&nwE, S, the Burren; parks, gardens; fp. cypresses, juniper

26 **Triple-spotted Pug** *E. trisignaria* H.-S.; J, Jy; E, W, seS; fens, roadsides, marshy areas; fp. wild angelica, hogweed (seeds)

27 **Satyr Pug** *E. satyrata* Hb.; My, J; nE, S, I, loc. sE & W; downland, moorland; fp. knapweed, Devil's-bit scabious (flowers)

28 **Wormwood Pug** *E. absinthiata* Clerck; J, Jy; T; woodland, waste ground; fp. compositae (flowers)

29 **Currant Pug** *E. assimilata* Doubl.; My, J, A; T; gardens, waste ground; fp. currants, wild hop

30 **Bleached Pug** *E. expallidata* Doubl.; J–A; sE, W, loc. nwE & sS; woodland; fp. goldenrod (flowers)

31 **Common Pug** *E. vulgata* Haw.

32 **Common Pug** *E. vulgata scotica* Cockayne; My, J, A; T; hedgerows, waste ground; fp. various incl. sallow, ragwort, hawthorn

33 **White-spotted Pug** *E. tripunctaria* H.-S.; My–A; E, sW, sS, I; woodland, roadsides; fp. elder (flowers), wild angelica (seeds)

34 **Campanula Pug** *E. denotata* Hb.

35 **Campanula Pug** *E. denotata jasioneata* Crewe; Jy; s&eE & sW (*denotata*), swE, W & I (*jasioneata*); woodland, downland; fp. nettle-leaved & giant bellflower (seeds)

36 **Bordered Pug** *E. succenturiata* Linn.; Jy, A; E, W, v. loc. S & I; commons, roadsides; fp. mugwort

37 **Grey Pug** *E. subfuscata* Haw.

38 **Grey Pug** *E. subfuscata* ab. *obscurissima* Prout; My, J, A; T; any habitat; fp. many trees & low-growing plants

39 **Tawny Speckled Pug** *E. icterata* Haw.

40 **Tawny Speckled Pug** *E. icterata cognata* Steph.; Jy, A; T; downland, roadsides, waste ground; fp. yarrow (flowers & leaves)

41 **Shaded Pug** *E. subumbrata* D. & S.; J, Jy; E, W, I; downland, grassy areas; fp. various incl. field scabious, ragwort (flowers)

42 **Yarrow Pug** *E. millefoliata* Rössler; J, Jy; seE; sand hills, roadsides; fp. yarrow (seeds)

43 **Plain Pug** *E. simpliciata* Haw.; J–A; c, s&wE, v. loc. W & I; waste ground, salt-marshes; fp. goosefoot, orache (seeds)

44 **Thyme Pug** *E. distinctaria* Guenée; J, Jy; cs, sw&wE, wW, wS, wI, Isle of Man; rocky coasts, sea-cliffs, limestone hills; fp. thyme (flowers)

45 **Ochreous Pug** *E. indigata* Hb.; Ap, My; T; pinewoods; fp. Scots pine (buds, young shoots)

46 **Pimpinel Pug** *E. pimpinellata* Hb.; J, Jy; s, e&cE to Yorks., v. loc. I; chalk downs, roadsides; fp. burnet saxifrage (seeds)

47 **Narrow-winged Pug** *E. nanata* Prout

48 **Narrow-winged Pug** *E. nanata* ab. *oliveri* Prout; Ap–J, Jy, A; T; heathland, moorland; fp. heather (flowers)

49 **Scarce Pug** *E. extensaria* Prout; J, Jy; v. loc. eE; salt-marsh edges; fp. sea wormwood (flowers & leaves)

50 **Ash Pug** *E. fraxinata* Crewe; My, J, A; T; woodland, hedgerows, sand hills; fp. ash, sea-buckthorn

51 **Golden-rod Pug** *E. virgaureata* Doubl.

52 **Golden-rod Pug** *E. virgaureata* ab. *nigra* Lempke; My, J, A; T; woodland, roadsides; fp. goldenrod, ragwort (flowers)

53 **Brindled Pug** *E. abbreviata* Steph.

54 **Brindled Pug** *E. abbreviata* ab. *hirschkei* Bastelberger; Ap, My; T except nS; woodland; fp. oak

55 **Oak-tree Pug** *E. dodoneata* Guen.; My, J; E, W, I; woodland, hedgerows; fp. oak, hawthorn

56 **Juniper Pug** *E. pusillata* D. & S.; Jy–Sp; T; chalk downs, parkland; fp. juniper

57 **Cypress Pug** *E. phoeniceata* Rambur; J–Sp; s&seE, sI; gardens, parks; fp. Monterey cypress

58 **The V-Pug** *Chloroclystis v-ata* Haw.; My–A; E, W, sS, I; waste ground, roadsides; fp. various incl. hemp agrimony, goldenrod (flowers)

59 **Larch Pug** *Eupithecia lariciata* Freyer

60 **Larch Pug** *Eupithecia lariciata* ab. *nigra* Prout; My, J; T; larch plantations; fp. larch

61 **Dwarf Pug** *E. tantillaria* Boisduval; My, J; E, W, S, loc. swI; conifer woods, parks, gardens; fp. Norway spruce, Douglas fir

62 **Sloe Pug** *Chloroclystis chloerata* Mabille; My, J; s&cE to Yorks.; hedgerows, bushy areas; fp. blackthorn (flowers)

63 **Green Pug** *C. rectangulata* Linn.

64 **Green Pug** *C. rectangulata* ab. *anthrax* Dietze; J, Jy; T; woodland, gardens, hedgerows; fp. blackthorn, fruit trees (flowers)

65 **Bilberry Pug** *C. debiliata* Hb.; J, Jy; s&wE, s&wW, I; woodland; fp. bilberry

66 **Double-striped Pug** *Gymnoscelis rufifasciata* Haw.; Ap, My, Jy, A; T; heathland, waste ground, gardens; fp. various incl. heathers, gorse, ragwort (flowers)

67 **Dentated Pug** *Anticollix sparsata* Treitschke; J, Jy; s&eE; fens, marshy areas, wet woodland; fp. yellow loosestrife

68 **Manchester Treble-bar** *Carsia sororiata* Prout; Jy, A; c, n&eE, S, c&wI; damp heathland, moorland; fp. bilberry, cowberry (flowers & leaves)

69 **Blomer's Rivulet** *Discoloxia blomeri* Curtis; My–Jy; loc. E, n&sW; woodland; fp. wych elm

70 **Dingy Shell** *Euchoeca nebulata* Scopoli; J, Jy; E, W; damp woodland, marshy areas; fp. alder

71 **Small White Wave** *Asthena albulata* Hufnagel; My–Jy, occ. A in sE; E, W, wS, w&nI; woodland; fp. birch, hazel

72 **Small Yellow Wave** *Hydrelia flammeolaria* Hufn.; J, Jy; E, W, wS; woodland, hedgerows; fp. maple, alder

73 **Drab Looper** *Minoa murinata* Scop.; My, J, occ. A; s&scE, seW; woodland; fp. wood spurge

74 **The Streak** *Chesias legatella* D. & S.; Sp, O; T; downland, heathland; fp. broom

75 **Broom-tip** *C. rufata* Fabr.; Ap–Jy; E, W, cS; downland, heathland; fp. broom

76 **Treble-bar** *Aplocera plagiata* Linn.; My, J, A, Sp (Jy, A in nE & S); T; downland, woodland, moorland; fp. St John's worts

77 **Lesser Treble-bar** *A. efformata* Guen.; My, J, A, Sp; E, W; downland, woodland, waste ground; fp. St John's worts

78 **Chimney Sweeper** *Odezia atrata* Linn.; J, Jy; T (v. loc. sE, East Anglia); chalk downs, damp meadows; fp. pignut (flowers)

79 **Grey Carpet** *Lithostege griseata* D. & S.; My–Jy; v. loc. Norfolk, Suffolk; Breck district; fp. flixweed, treacle mustard (seedpods)

80 **Welsh Wave** *Venusia cambrica* Curtis

81 **Welsh Wave** *Venusia cambrica* f. *bradyi* Prout; J–A; sw,c&nE, W, S, I; woodland, mountain moorland; fp. rowan

82 **Waved Carpet** *Hydrelia sylvata* D. & S.; J, Jy; loc. s, sw, c&nwE, se&wI; woodland; fp. birch, sallow, sweet chestnut

83 **The Seraphim** *Lobophora halterata* Hufn.; My, J; T; woodland; fp. aspen

84 **Barred Tooth-striped** *Trichopteryx polycommata* D. & S.; M, Ap; E (except sw), wS; downland, bushy areas; fp. wild privet, ash

PLATE 8: *Geometridae*

Geometridae (Larentiinae)

1 **Early Tooth-striped** *Trichopteryx carpinata* Borkhausen; Ap, My; T; woodland; fp. sallow, birch, honeysuckle

2 **Small Seraphim** *Pterapherapteryx sexalata* Retzius; My–A; sE, East Anglia, loc. c&nE & cS & wI; damp woodland, marshy areas; fp. sallow

3 **Yellow-barred Brindle** *Acasis viretata* Hübner; My, J also Jy–A in s; sE, W, I, loc. nwE & wS; woodland, hedgerows; fp. wild privet, ivy, holly (flowers & leaves)

Geometridae (Ennominae)

4 **Clouded Border** *Lomaspilis marginata* Linnaeus; J–A; T; damp woodland, marshy areas; fp. sallows, aspen

5 **Scorched Carpet** *Ligdia adustata* Denis & Schiffermüller; My, J, Jy, A (in sE), J (in n); E, W, I, v. loc. c&neE; hedgerows, bushy areas; fp. spindle

6 **The V-Moth** *Semiothisa wauaria* Linn.; Jy, A; E, W, I, S to Moray; gardens, orchards; fp. currants, gooseberry

7 **The Magpie** *Abraxas grossulariata* Linn.; Jy, A; T; gardens, woodland, hedgerows; fp. currants, gooseberry, hawthorn, hazel

8 **Clouded Magpie** *A. sylvata* Scopoli; My–Jy; E, W, sS, sI; woodland, parks; fp. wych elm, English elm

9 **Brown Silver-line** *Petrophora chlorosata* Scop.; My, J; T; woodland, heathland; fp. bracken

10 **Scorched Wing** *Plagodis dolabraria* Linn.; My–Jy; E. W, I, swS; woodland; fp. oak, sallow, birch

11 **Netted Mountain Moth** *Semiothisa carbonaria* Clerck; Ap–J; loc. in Scottish Highlands; mountainsides, moorland; fp. bearberry

12 **Peacock Moth** *S. notata* Linn.; My, J also Jy, A in sE; s&cE, East Anglia, W, s&wS, swI; woodland; fp. birch

13 **Sharp-angled Peacock** *S. alternaria* Hb.; My–Jy, A; s&eE, sW; woodland, sand hills; fp. sallow, blackthorn, sea buckthorn

14 **Tawny-barred Angle** *S. liturata* Cl.

15 **Tawny-barred Angle** *S. liturata* f. *nigrofulvata* Collins; J, Jy also A, Sp in sE; T; conifer woods; fp. Scots pine, Norway spruce

16 **Latticed Heath** *S. clathrata* Linn.

17 **Latticed Heath** *S. clathrata* ab. *alboguttata* Fettig; My, J, Jy–Sp; E, W, sS, n&wI; downland, heathland, waste ground; fp. lucerne, clovers, trefoils

18 **Rannoch Looper** *S. brunneata* Thunberg; J, Jy; res. c&neS, mig. eE & seS; open woodland; fp. bilberry

19 **Little Thorn** *Cepphis advenaria* Hb.; My, J; s&cE, seW, swI; woodland; fp. bilberry

20 **Horse Chestnut** *Pachycnemia hippocastanaria* Hb. ♂

21 **Horse Chestnut** *Pachycnemia hippocastanaria* Hb. ♀; M–Sp; sE, sW; heathland; fp. heather

22 **Speckled Yellow** *Pseudopanthera macularia* Linn.; My, J; T; woodland; fp. wood sage

23 **Barred Umber** *Plagodis pulveraria* Linn.; My, J; T; woodland; fp. birch, sallow

24 **Brimstone Moth** *Opisthograptis luteolata* Linn.; Ap–O; T; woodland, hedgerows, bushy areas; fp. various incl. hawthorn, hazel

25 **Bordered Beauty** *Epione repandaria* Hufnagel; Jy–Sp; T; damp woodland, marshy areas; fp. sallows

26 **Dark Bordered Beauty** *E. paralellaria* D. & S. ♂

27 **Dark Bordered Beauty** *E. paralellaria* D. & S. ♀; Jy, A; v. loc. neE & s&cS; wet heathland; fp. creeping willow

28 **Lilac Beauty** *Apeira syringaria* Linn.; J, Jy; E, W, I; woodland; fp. honeysuckle, wild privet

29 **Large Thorn** *Ennomos autumnaria* Werneburg ♂

30 **Large Thorn** *Ennomos autumnaria* Werneburg ♀; Sp, O; loc. seE, East Anglia; woodland, bushy areas; fp. trees incl. birch, oak, hawthorn

31 **Canary-shouldered Thorn** *E. alniaria* Linn.; Jy–O; T; woodland, marshy areas; fp. trees incl. birch, sallow, alder

32 **August Thorn** *E. quercinaria* Hufn. ♂

33 **August Thorn** *E. quercinaria* Hufn. ♀; Jy–Sp; E, W, I, Isle of Man, loc. in S; woodland, fp. trees incl. birch, oak, hawthorn

34 **Dusky Thorn** *E. fuscantaria* Haworth; Jy–O; E, W; woodland, parks; fp. ash

35 **September Thorn** *E. erosaria* D. & S.; Jy–O; E, W, S to Inverness; woodland, parks; fp. oak, birch, lime

36 **Early Thorn** *Selenia dentaria* Fabricius (spring) ♂

37 **Early Thorn** *Selenia dentaria* Fabricius (spring) ♀

38 **Early Thorn** *Selenia dentaria* Fabricius (summer) ♂

39 **Early Thorn** *Selenia dentaria* Fabricius (summer) ♀; spring Ap, My, summer Jy–Sp; T; woodland, hedgerows; fp. trees incl. birch, sallow, hawthorn

40 **Lunar Thorn** *S. lunularia* Hb.; My, J; T; woodland; fp. trees incl. oak, birch, ash

41 **Purple Thorn** *S. tetralunaria* Hufn. (spring)

42 **Purple Thorn** *S. tetralunaria* Hufn. (summer); spring My, J, summer Jy, A, My in n; sE, W, loc. in nE & S; woodland, downland, heathland; fp. trees incl. birch, oak, sallow

43 **Scalloped Oak** *Crocallis elinguaria* Linn.; Jy, A; T; woodland, downland, hedgerows; fp. most deciduous trees & shrubs

PLATE 9: *Geometridae*

Geometridae (Ennominae)

1 **Scalloped Hazel** *Odontopera bidentata* Clerck

2 **Scalloped Hazel** *Odontopera bidentata* Clerck; My, J; T; woodland, hedgerows, heathland, fp. incl. oak, birch, pine, hawthorn

3 **Swallow-tailed Moth** *Ourapteryx sambucaria* Linnaeus; J, Jy; E, W, I, sS, loc. nS; woodland, hedgerows, gardens; fp. ivy, various trees & shrubs

4 **Feathered Thorn** *Colotois pennaria* Linn.

5 **Feathered Thorn** *Colotois pennaria* Linn.; O, N; T; woodland, heathland, bushy areas; fp. incl. oak, birch, hawthorn

6 **Small Brindled Beauty** *Apocheima hispidaria* Denis & Schiffermüller ♂

7 **Small Brindled Beauty** *Apocheima hispidaria* Denis & Schiffermüller ♀; F–Ap; E, W; woodland; fp. oak, hazel

8 **Orange Moth** *Angerona prunaria* Linn. ♂

9 **Orange Moth** *Angerona prunaria* Linn. ♀

10 **Orange Moth** *Angerona prunaria* f. *corylaria* Thunberg ♂

11 **Orange Moth** *Angerona prunaria* f. *corylaria* Thunberg ♀; J, Jy; sE, seW, sI; woodland, heathland, fp. incl: hawthorn, heather, birch

12 **Pale Brindled Beauty** *Apocheima pilosaria* D. & S. ♂

13 **Pale Brindled Beauty** *Apocheima pilosaria* f. *monacharia* Staudinger

14 **Pale Brindled Beauty** *Apocheima pilosaria* D. & S. ♀; Ja–M; T; woodland, hedgerows; fp. trees & shrubs incl. birch, oak, hawthorn

15 **Brindled Beauty** *Lycia hirtaria* Cl.; M–My; s&cE, sW, v. loc. nE, nW, S, & I; woodland, parks, gardens; fp. trees incl. birch, lime, hawthorn

16 **Belted Beauty** *L. zonaria* Harrison ♂

17 **Belted Beauty** *L. zonaria* Harrison ♀; M, Ap; loc. nW, Wirral, w Argyll, Hebrides, wI; coastal sand hills; fp. incl. bird's-foot trefoil, clover, plantain

18 **Rannoch Brindled Beauty** *L. lapponaria* Harr. ♂

19 **Rannoch Brindled Beauty** *L. lapponaria* Harr. ♀; Ap; cS; boggy moorland; fp. bog myrtle, heathers

20 **Peppered Moth** *Biston betularia* Linn.

21 **Peppered Moth** *Biston betularia* f. *insularia* Thierry-Mieg

22 **Peppered Moth** *Biston betularia* f. *carbonaria* Jordan; My–A; T; woodland, parks; fp. incl. birch, sallow, oak

23 **Oak Beauty** *B. strataria* Hufnagel; M, Ap; E, W, I, sS; woodland, parks; fp. trees incl. oak, hazel, aspen

24 **Mottled Umber** *Erannis defoliaria* Cl. ♂

25 **Mottled Umber** *Erannis defoliaria* Cl. ♂

26 **Mottled Umber** *Erannis defoliaria* Cl. ♀; O–D; T; woodland, hedgerows, bushy areas; fp. trees & shrubs incl. hawthorn, birch, oak

27 **Spring Usher** *Agriopis leucophaearia* D. & S. ♂

28 **Spring Usher** *Agriopis leucophaearia* D. & S. ♂

29 **Spring Usher** *Agriopis leucophaearia* D. & S. ♀; Ja–M; E, W, loc. in sS; woodland, parks; fp. oak

30 **Scarce Umber** *A. aurantiaria* Hübner ♂

31 **Scarce Umber** *A. aurantiaria* Hübner ♀; O, N; E, W, S, nI; woodland, bushy areas; fp. hazel, oak, birch

32 **Dotted Border** *A. marginaria* Fabricius ♂

33 **Dotted Border** *A. marginaria* Fabricius ♀; F–Ap; T; woodland, hedgerows, bushy areas; fp. incl. hawthorn, birch, oak

PLATE 10: *Geometridae*

Geometridae (Ennominae)

1 **Waved Umber** *Menophra abruptaria* Thunberg

2 **Waved Umber** *Menophra abruptaria* ab. *fuscata* Tutt; Ap–J; E, W; woodland, parks, gardens; fp. privet, lilac

3 **Willow Beauty** *Peribatodes rhomboidaria* Denis & Schiffermüller

4 **Willow Beauty** *Peribatodes rhomboidaria* f. *perfumaria* Newman; J–A, occ. also Sp in sE; T; woodland, hedgerows, gardens; fp. incl. birch, hawthorn, garden privet

5 **Feathered Beauty** *P. secundaria* Esper; Jy, A; Kent, w Sussex; conifer woods; fp. Norway spruce

6 **Bordered Grey** *Selidosema brunnearia* Staudinger; Jy, A; loc. s&neE, wW, Argyll, Kincardine, Isle of Man; heathland, downland; fp. bird's-foot trefoil, heather

7 **Satin Beauty** *Deileptenia ribeata* Clerck

8 **Satin Beauty** *Deileptenia ribeata* f, *nigra* Cockayne; J–A; E, W, swS, seI; woodland; fp. oak, birch, pine, yew, spruce

9 **Ringed Carpet** *Cleora cinctaria* D. & S.; Ap, My; csE, nwW, S, I; heathland; fp. birch, heath, bilberry

10 **Mottled Beauty** *Alcis repandata* Linnaeus

11 **Mottled Beauty** *Alcis repandata* Linnaeus; J–A; T; woodland, moorland, bushy areas; fp. incl. birch, oak, bilberry, hawthorn

12 **Square Spot** *Paradarisa consonaria* Hübner; Ap–J; s,c&nwE, W, swI; woodland; fp. oak, pine, yew, birch

13 **Dotted Carpet** *Alcis jubata* Thunb.; Jy, A; s,sw&neE, W, sS; woodland; fp. beard lichen

14 **Great Oak Beauty** *Boarmia roboraria* D. & S.

15 **Great Oak Beauty** *Boarmia roboraria* ab. *infuscata* Stdgr; J, Jy; s&cE, seW; woodland; fp. oak

16 **Brussels Lace** *Cleorodes lichenaria* Hufnagel; J–A; sE, W, sS, I; woodland; fp. lichens on oak & blackthorn

17 **Pale Oak Beauty** *Serraca punctinalis* Scopoli

18 **Pale Oak Beauty** *Serraca punctinalis* ab. *humperti* Humpert; My–A; sE, W; woodland; fp. oak, birch

19 **Small Engrailed** *Ectropis crepuscularia* D. & S.

20 **Small Engrailed** *Ectropis crepuscularia* D. & S. (melanic); My, J; E, W, I, sS; woodland, bushy areas; fp. birch, sallow, larch

21 **The Engrailed** *E. bistortata* Goeze; M, Ap, J–A (Ap, My in n); E, W, S, swI; woodland, bushy areas; fp. trees & shrubs incl. birch, sallow, oak

22 **Brindled White-spot** *Paradarisa extersaria* Hb.; My, J; s&cE, East Anglia, W; woodland; fp. oak, birch

23 **Grey Birch** *Aethalura punctulata* D. & S.; My, J; E, W, loc. in sS & I; woodland; fp. birch

24 **Common Heath** *Ematurga atomaria* Linn.

25 **Common Heath** *Ematurga atomaria* Linn.; My–Jy, A; T; heathland, downland, woodland; fp. heathers, clovers, trefoils

26 **Bordered White** *Bupalus piniaria* Linn. (south) ♂

27 **Bordered White** *Bupalus piniaria* Linn. (south) ♀

28 **Bordered White** *Bupalus piniaria* Linn. (north) ♂

29 **Bordered White** *Bupalus piniaria* Linn. (north) ♀; My–Jy (later in n); T; coniferous woodland; fp. pines

30 **Sloe Carpet** *Aleucis distinctata* Herrich-Schäffer; Ap; loc. s&seE; hedgerows; fp. blackthorn

31 **Common White Wave** *Cabera pusaria* Linn.; My, J, Jy, A (in s), My–Jy (in n); T; woodland, bushy areas; fp. birch, hazel, sallow

32 **Common Wave** *C. exanthemata* Scop.; My–Jy, also Jy–Sp in s; T; damp woodland, fens; fp. sallow, aspen

33 **White-pinion Spotted** *Lomographa bimaculata* Fabricius; My, J; s&nwE, East Anglia, sW, sI; woodland, hedgerows; fp. hawthorn, blackthorn

34 **Clouded Silver** *L. temerata* D. & S.; My–Jy; E, W, I, swS; woodland, hedgerows; fp. hawthorn, blackthorn

35 **Early Moth** *Theria primaria* Haworth ♂

36 **Early Moth** *Theria primaria* Haworth ♀; Ja, F; E, W, nI, v. loc. sS; hedgerows, bushy areas; fp. hawthorn, blackthorn

PLATE 11: *Geometridae, Sphingidae*

Geometridae (Ennominae)

1 **Light Emerald** *Campaea margaritata* Linnaeus; Jy, A also A, Sp in s; T; woodland; fp. trees incl. oak, birch, hawthorn

2 **Barred Red** *Hylaea fasciaria* Linn.

3 **Barred Red** *Hylaea fasciaria* ab. *grisearia* Fuchs; J–A; T; conifer woods; fp. Scots pine, Norway spruce

4 **Scotch Annulet** *Gnophos obfuscatus* Denis & Schiffermüller; Jy, A; c&nS, wI; moorland, mountainsides; fp. heather

5 **The Annulet** *G. obscuratus* D. & S. (chalk)

6 **The Annulet** *G. obscuratus* D. & S. (heath); Jy, A; coastal T, inland sE & sW; heathland, downland, coastal rocky areas; fp. heather, bird's-foot trefoil, common rock-rose

7 **Black-veined Moth** *Siona lineata* Scopoli; My, J; v. loc. Kent; downland, grassy banks; fp. unrecorded (in captivity – dock)

8 **Grey Scalloped Bar** *Dyscia fagaria* Thunberg; My–A; s,c&nE, nW, S, I; heathland, moorland; fp. heathers

9 **Straw Belle** *Aspitates gilvaria* D. & S.; Jy, A; v. loc. seE, the Burren; chalk downs; fp. thyme, cinquefoils

10 **Yellow Belle** *A. ochrearia* Rossi; My, J, A, Sp; sE, East Anglia; waste ground, sand hills, saltmarsh edges; fp. buck's horn plantain, wild carrot

11 **Black Mountain Moth** *Psodos coracina* Esper ♂

12 **Black Mountain Moth** *Psodos coracina* Esper ♀; Jy; Scottish Highlands; mountains above 600 m; fp. crowberry

13 **Grass Wave** *Perconia strigillaria* Hübner; J, Jy; E, W, I, sS; heathland, woodland, commons; fp. heather, broom

Sphingidae (Sphinginae)

14 **Death's-head Hawk-moth** *Acherontia atropos* Linn.; My–Sp; mig. T; fp. potato (leaves)

15 **Lime Hawk-moth** *Mimas tiliae* Linn.; My–Jy; s&cE, eW; woodland, parks, urban areas; fp. lime, English elm, alder

16 **Convolvulus Hawk-moth** *Agrius convolvuli* Linn.; Jy–N; mig. T; fp. convolvulus

Sphingidae (Macroglossinae)

17 **Spurge Hawk-moth** *Hyles euphorbiae* Linn.; My–Sp; mig. v. loc. sE; fp. spurges

18 **Bedstraw Hawk-moth** *H. gallii* Rottemburg; My–A; mig. loc. T; fp. bedstraws

19 **Narrow-bordered Bee Hawk-moth** *Hemaris tityus* Linn.; My, J; v. loc. T; woodland, marshy areas; fp. devil's-bit scabious

20 **Broad-bordered Bee Hawk-moth** *H. fuciformis* Linn.; My, J; loc. s&cE; woodland; fp. honeysuckle

21 **Humming-bird Hawk-moth** *Macroglossum stellatarum* Linn.; My–O; mig. T; fp. bedstraws, wild madder

PLATE 12: *Sphingidae*

Sphingidae (Sphinginae)

1 **Privet Hawk-moth** *Sphinx ligustri* Linnaeus; J, Jy; s&seE, s&wW; woodland, gardens; fp. privet, lilac

2 **Pine Hawk-moth** *Hyloicus pinastri* Linn.; J–A; cs&seE, East Anglia; pinewoods, heathland with pines; fp. Scots pine, Norway spruce

3 **Eyed Hawk-moth** *Smerinthus ocellata* Linn.; My–Jy; E, W, I; woodland, gardens, orchards; fp. willow, sallow, apple

4 **Poplar Hawk-moth** *Laothoe populi* Linn.; My–Jy, occ. A & Sp; T; woodland edges, parks, damp areas; fp. poplar, sallow, willow

Sphingidae (Macroglossinae)

5 **Oleander Hawk-moth** *Daphnis nerii* Linn.; A–O; mig. sE; fp. periwinkle (in captivity – garden privet)

6 **Striped Hawk-moth** *Hyles lineata* Esper; My–O; mig. loc. T; fp. hedge bedstraw

7 **Elephant Hawk-moth** *Deilephila elpenor* Linn.; My–Jy, occ. A; E, W, I, loc. in S; rough ground, river valleys, gardens; fp. willowherbs, fuchsia

8 **Silver-striped Hawk-moth** *Hippotion celerio* Linn.; A–N; mig. E; fp. bedstraws, grapevine, fuchsia

9 **Small Elephant Hawk-moth** *Deilephila porcellus* Linn.; My–Jy; T; chalk downs, heathland, coastal sand hills; fp. bedstraws

PLATE 13: *Notodontidae*

1 **Buff-tip** *Phalera bucephala* Linnaeus; My–Jy; T; woodland, parks; fp. trees incl. oak, lime, sallow, birch
2 **Alder Kitten** *Furcula bicuspis* Borkhausen; My–Jy; se, sw, cE, East Anglia, W; woodland, fp. alder, birch
3 **Sallow Kitten** *F. furcula* Clerck; My, J, A (E, W) J, Jy (S, I.); T; woodland, heathland; fp. sallows, aspen
4 **Poplar Kitten** *F. bifida* Brahm; My–Jy; E, W; vicinity of poplars; fp. poplar, aspen
5 **Puss Moth** *Cerura vinula* Linn.; My–Jy; T; woodland, hedgerows; fp. sallows, poplars
6 **Iron Prominent** *Notodonta dromedarius* Linn.; My–Jy, A, Sp; T; woodland; fp. birch, hazel, oak
7 **Coxcomb Prominent** *Ptilodon capucina* Linn.; My, J, A, Sp; T; woodland, hedgerows; fp. trees incl. birch, hazel, sallows
8 **Lobster Moth** *Stauropus fagi* Linn.
9 **Lobster Moth** *Stauropus fagi* f. *obscura* Rebel; My–Jy; s&scE, W, swI; woodland; fp. beech, oak, birch
10 **Pebble Prominent** *Eligmodonta ziczac* Linn.; My, J, Jy, A in s, J, Jy in n; T; woodland, hedgerows; fp. sallow, willow
11 **Lesser Swallow Prominent** *Pheosia gnoma* Fabricius; My, J, Jy, A; T; woodland; fp. birch
12 **Swallow Prominent** *P. tremula* Cl.; My, J, Jy, A in s, J, Jy in n; T; woodland; fp. poplar, sallow, willow
13 **Great Prominent** *Peridea anceps* Goeze; Ap–J; s&scE, Lake District, W, S to Perthshire; woodland; fp. oak
14 **Scarce Prominent** *Odontosia carmelita* Esper
15 **Scarce Prominent** *Odontosia carmelita* Esper (Scottish); Ap, My; s,se,w&nE, cS, loc. in e&swI; woodland; fp. birch
16 **Maple Prominent** *Ptilodontella cucullina* Denis & Schiffermüller; My–Jy; sE, East Anglia; woodland, chalk downs; fp. field maple
17 **White Prominent** *Leucodonta bicoloria* D. & S.; My–Jy; v. loc. swI; woodland; fp. birch
18 **Pale Prominent** *Pterostoma palpina* Cl., My, J, also Jy, A in s; T; woodland, parks; fp. poplar, aspen, willow
19 **Plumed Prominent** *Ptilophora plumigera* D. & S. ♂
20 **Plumed Prominent** *Ptilophora plumigera* D. & S. ♀; N, D; v. loc. sE; woodland on chalk; fp. field maple
21 **Figure of Eight** *Diloba caeruleocephala* Linn.; O, N; E, W, loc. in S & I; woodland, hedgerows; fp. blackthorn, hawthorn

PLATE 14: *Notodontidae, Lymantriidae, Arctiidae*

Notodontidae

1 **Marbled Brown** *Drymonia dodonaea* Denis & Schiffermüller; My–Jy; E, W, wS, swI; woodland; fp. oak

2 **Lunar Marbled Brown** *D. ruficornis* Hufnagel; Ap, My; E, W, s&cS, swI; woodland; fp. oak

3 **Scarce Chocolate-tip** *Clostera anachoreta* D. & S.; Ap, My, A; v. loc. seE; woodland; fp. sallow, aspen, poplar

4 **Chocolate-tip** *C. curtula* Linnaeus; Ap, My, A, Sp (J, Jy in S); s&seE, seW, loc. S; woodland, parks; fp. poplar, sallow, willow

5 **Small Chocolate-tip** *C. pigra* Hufn.; My, A (J, Jy in nE & S); T; marshy areas, fens; fp. creeping willow, sallow

Lymantriidae

6 **Scarce Vapourer** *Orgyia recens* Hübner ♂

7 **Scarce Vapourer** *Orgyia recens* Hübner ♀; J, Jy, A–O; v. loc. Yorks. Lincs. Norfolk; woodland, hedgerows; fp. hawthorn, oak, bramble

8 **The Vapourer** *O. antiqua* Linn. ♂

9 **The Vapourer** *O. antiqua* Linn. ♀; J, Jy, Sp, O; T; woodland, hedgerows, gardens; fp. most deciduous trees & shrubs

10 **Dark Tussock** *Dicallomera fascelina* Linn. ♂

11 **Dark Tussock** *Dicallomera fascelina* Linn. ♀; Jy, A; s&nE, cS, loc. in nI; heathland, coastal sand hills; fp. heather, hawthorn, sallow

12 **Pale Tussock** *Calliteara pudibunda* Linn. ♀

13 **Pale Tussock** *Calliteara pudibunda* Linn. ♂; My, J; E, W, sI; woodland, hedgerows; fp. trees incl. oak, birch, hazel

14 **Black Arches** *Lymantria monacha* Linn. ♂

15 **Black Arches** *Lymantria monacha* Linn. ♀; Jy, A; sE, W; woodland; fp. oak

16 **Brown-tail** *Euproctis chrysorrhoea* Linn.; Jy, A; s,se&eE; hedgerows, bushy areas; fp. hawthorn, blackthorn, oak

17 **Yellow-tail** *E. similis* Fuessly ♂

18 **Yellow-tail** *E. similis* Fuessly ♀; Jy, A; E, W, v. loc. sS & wI; hedgerows, bushy areas; fp. hawthorn, blackthorn, sallow

19 **White Satin Moth** *Leucoma salicis* Linn.; J–A; E, eW, v. loc. eI; woodland, parks; fp. poplar, sallow, willow

Arctiidae (Lithosiinae)

20 **Round-winged Muslin** *Thumatha senex* Hb.; Jy, A; E, W, loc. S & I; marshy areas, fens; fp. lichens

21 **Dew Moth** *Setina irrorella* Linn.; J, Jy; s&seE, wW, wS, the Burren, Isle of Man; shingle beaches, chalk hills, rocky cliffs; fp. lichens on rocks

22 **Muslin Footman** *Nudaria mundana* Linn.; J–A; T. to Scottish Highlands; rocky areas, stone walls; fp. lichens on rocks & stones

23 **Rosy Footman** *Miltochrista miniata* Forster; J–A; sE, East Anglia, W, sI; woodland, hedgerows; fp. lichens on trees

24 **Red-necked Footman** *Atolmis rubricollis* Linn.; My–Jy; loc. W & sE & sI; woodland; fp. lichens on trees

25 **Dotted Footman** *Pelosia muscerda* Hufn.; Jy, A; Norfolk; marshes, carrs; fp. unrecorded

26 **Four-dotted Footman** *Cybosia mesomella* Linn.

27 **Four-dotted Footman** *Cybosia mesomella* ab. *flava* de Graaf; J–A; E, W, loc. S; heathland, woodland; fp. lichens

28 **Small Dotted Footman** *Pelosia obtusa* Herrich-Schäffer; Jy, A; v. loc. Norfolk; reed-beds; fp. unrecorded

29 **Orange Footman** *Eilema sororcula* Hufn.; My, J; s&seE, East Anglia, sW; woodland; fp. lichens on beech & oak

30 **Hoary Footman** *E. caniola* Hb.; Jy–Sp; swE, s&wW, occ. seE; sea-cliffs, shingle beaches; fp. lichens on rocks

31 **Northern Footman** *E. sericea* Gregson; Jy; nwE, nW, Isle of Man; boggy moorland; fp. lichens

32 **Four-spotted Footman** *Lithosia quadra* Linn. ♂

33 **Four-spotted Footman** *Lithosia quadra* Linn. ♀; Jy–Sp; res. sE & I, mig. T; woodland; fp. lichens on trees

34 **Dingy Footman** *Eilema griseola* Hb.

35 **Dingy Footman** *Eilema griseola* ab. *stramineola* Doubleday; Jy, A; s&cE, W; fens, marshes, damp woodland; fp. lichens

36 **Scarce Footman** *E. complana* Linn.; Jy, A; s&cE, W, loc. s&wI; heathland, woodland, downland; fp. lichens

37 **Common Footman** *E. lurideola* Zincken; J–A; E, W, I; loc. S; woodland, bushy areas, hedgerows; fp. lichens on trees & fences

38 **Pigmy Footman** *E. pygmaeola* Doubl.; Jy, A; Kent, Norfolk; coastal sand hills; fp. lichens

PLATE 15: *Arctiidae, Nolidae, Noctuidae*

Arctiidae (Lithosiinae)
1 **Buff Footman** *Eilema deplana* Esper; Jy, A; sE, W, swI; woodland, bushy downs; fp. lichens on trees & shrubs

Arctiidae (Arctiinae)
2 **Speckled Footman** *Coscinia cribraria* South; Jy, A; v. loc. Dorset, Hants; heathland; fp. uncertain
3 **Wood Tiger** *Parasemia plantaginis* Linnaeus; My–Jy; T, except seE; downland, woodland, heathland; fp. low-growing plants incl. plantain
4 **Scarlet Tiger** *Callimorpha dominula* Linn.; J, Jy; v. loc. s&wE, s&wW; water meadows, marshy areas; fp. comfrey, common nettle, meadowsweet
5 **Garden Tiger** *Arctia caja* Linn.; Jy, A; T; woodland, roadsides, gardens; fp. many low-growing plants
6 **Jersey Tiger** *Euplagia quadripunctaria* Poda; Jy–Sp; s Devon, Channel Islands; waste ground, gardens; fp. dandelion, plantain, nettle
7 **The Cinnabar** *Tyria jacobaeae* Linn.; My–Jy; T, loc. sS; grassland, waste ground, heathland; fp. common ragwort, groundsel
8 **Cream-spot Tiger** *Arctia villica* Oberthür; My–Jy; sE, sW; coastal cliffs, downland, woodland; fp. polyphagous on low-growing plants
9 **Clouded Buff** *Diacrisia sannio* Linn. ♂
10 **Clouded Buff** *Diacrisia sannio* Linn. ♀; J, Jy; T; heathland, chalk downs, woodland; fp. low-growing plants incl. heather, dandelion
11 **Ruby Tiger** *Phragmatobia fuliginosa* Linn.; Ap–J, Jy–Sp (J in S); T; woodland, moorland, grassy areas; fp. dock, dandelion, plantain
12 **White Ermine** *Spilosoma lubricipeda* Linn.
13 **White Ermine** *Spilosoma lubricipeda* Linn.; My–Jy; T; waste ground, gardens, woodland; fp. many low-growing plants
14 **Buff Ermine** *S. luteum* Hufnagel; My–Jy; T; waste ground, gardens, woodland; fp. many low-growing plants
15 **Water Ermine** *S. urticae* Esp.; J, Jy; loc. s&seE, East Anglia; water meadows, fens; fp. yellow loosestrife, mint, yellow iris
16 **Muslin Moth** *Diaphora mendica* Clerck ♂
17 **Muslin Moth** *Diaphora mendica* Clerck ♀; My, J; T to cS; downland, woodland, gardens; fp. dock, dandelion, chickweed

Nolidae
18 **Small Black Arches** *Meganola strigula* Denis & Schiffermüller; J, Jy; loc. sE, sW; woodland; fp. unrecorded (possibly oak)
19 **Kent Black Arches** *M. albula* D. & S.; J–A; loc. s&eE, wW; woodland, coastal areas; fp. dewberry
20 **Short-cloaked Moth** *Nola cucullatella* Linn.; J, Jy; E, W; woodland, hedgerows, bushy areas; fp. hawthorn, blackthorn
21 **Least Black Arches** *N. confusalis* Herrich-Schäffer; My, J; loc. T; woodland, parks; fp. lichens on trees

Noctuidae (Noctuinae)
22 **Square-spot Dart** *Euxoa obelisca* Tutt; A, Sp; coastal s&wE&W, S, s&wI; coastal cliffs; fp. unrecorded
23 **White-line Dart** *E. tritici* Linn.
24 **White-line Dart** *E. tritici* Linn.; Jy, A; T; heathland, coastal sand hills; fp. mouse-ears, chickweed
25 **Garden Dart** *E. nigricans* Linn.
26 **Garden Dart** *E. nigricans* Linn.; Jy, A; T; gardens, waste ground, marshy areas; fp. clovers, plantain, lettuce
27 **Coast Dart** *E. cursoria* Hufn.
28 **Coast Dart** *E. cursoria* Hufn.
29 **Coast Dart** *E. cursoria* Hufn.; Jy–Sp; coastal e&wE, S, n&wI; sand hills; fp. sea sandwort, sand-couch
30 **Light Feathered Rustic** *Agrotis cinerea* D. & S.
31 **Light Feathered Rustic** *Agrotis cinerea* D. & S.; My, J; loc. sE & W & swI; chalk downs, sea-cliffs, mountainsides; fp. wild thyme
32 **Archer's Dart** *A. vestigialis* Hufn.; Jy–Sp; coastal T, v. loc. inland; coastal sand hills, heathland; fp. grasses, bedstraws
33 **Turnip Moth** *A. segetum* D. & S.; My, J, A, Sp; T, loc. S; gardens, agricultural land, waste ground; fp. root vegetables (roots & stems)

PLATE 16: *Noctuidae*

Noctuidae (Noctuinae)

1 **Heart and Club** *Agrotis clavis* Hufnagel; J, Jy; T; waste ground, coastal sand hills; fp. clovers, dock, knotgrass (leaves & roots)

2 **Heart and Dart** *A. exclamationis* Linnaeus; My–Jy; T; agricultural land, gardens, waste ground; fp. various incl. dock, turnips (leaves, roots, stems)

3 **Crescent Dart** *A. trux* Stephens ♂

4 **Crescent Dart** *A. trux* Stephens ♀; Jy, A; coastal s&swE, wW, swI, Isle of Man; cliffs; fp. unrecorded (in captivity – dandelion)

5 **Dark Sword-grass** *A. ipsilon* Hufn.

6 **Dark Sword-grass** *A. ipsilon* Hufn.; M–N; mig. T; waste ground, grassy areas, gardens; fp. unrecorded (in captivity – dandelion)

7 **Shuttle-shaped Dart** *A. puta* Hübner ♂

8 **Shuttle-shaped Dart** *A. puta* Hübner ♀; Ap–O; s&cE, W; woodland, waste ground, marshy areas; fp. various incl. dock, dandelion

9 **Sand Dart** *A. ripae* Hb. (Kent)

10 **Sand Dart** *A. ripae* Hb. (Lancs.); J, Jy; coastal; E, W, eS, s&eI, Isle of Man; sand hills; fp. prickly saltwort, sea rocket

11 **Great Dart** *A. crassa* Hb.; A; Channel Islands; marshy areas; fp. grasses (roots)

12 **The Flame** *Axylia putris* Linn.; J, Jy occ. Sp, O; T (loc. S); hedgerows, wood edges, gardens; fp. various incl. dock, bedstraws, plantain

13 **Portland Moth** *Ochropleura praecox* Linn.; A, Sp; coastal E & W & S & I & Isle of Man, inland eE & eS; coastal sand hills, sandy heaths; fp. creeping willow, other sand hill plants

14 **Flame Shoulder** *O. plecta* Linn.; Ap–Jy, A, Sp; T; woodland, gardens, meadows; fp. various incl. dock, plantain, bedstraws

15 **Northern Rustic** *Standfussiana lucernea* Linn.

16 **Northern Rustic** *Standfussiana lucernea* Linn.; J–Sp; W, c, sw&nwE, Kent, S, I, Isle of Man; coastal cliffs, rocky mountainsides; fp. various incl. grasses, saxifrages

17 **Plain Clay** *Eugnorisma depuncta* Linn.; Jy–Sp; loc. W, sw&nE, c&eS; woodland; fp. dock, nettle, stitchwort

18 **Dotted Rustic** *Rhyacia simulans* Hufn.; J, Jy, A–O; E, nW, cS; chalk downs, moorlands; fp. unrecorded

19 **Stout Dart** *Spaelotis ravida* Denis & Schiffermüller; Jy–Sp; E, cW; damp meadows, marshy areas; fp. unrecorded (in captivity – dandelion)

20 **Rosy Marsh Moth** *Eugraphe subrosea* Steph.; Jy, A; v. loc. W; acid bogs, fens; fp. bog myrtle

21 **Large Yellow Underwing** *Noctua pronuba* Linn. ♂

22 **Large Yellow Underwing** *Noctua pronuba* Linn. ♀; J–Sp; T; any type of habitat; fp. various incl. chickweed, dandelion

23 **Lunar Yellow Underwing** *N. orbona* Hufn.; J–Sp; loc. s&eE, S: woodland, moorland, sand hills; fp. grasses, small herbaceous plants

24 **Broad-bordered Yellow Underwing** *N. fimbriata* Schreber ♂

25 **Broad-bordered Yellow Underwing** *N. fimbriata* Schreber ♀; Jy–Sp; T; woodland, parks; fp. sallow, blackthorn, dock

26 **Lesser Yellow Underwing** *N. comes* Hb.; Jy–Sp; T; hedgerows, heathland, woodland; fp. sallow, blackthorn, heather, dock

27 **Lesser Broad-bordered Yellow Underwing** *N. janthina* D. & S.; Jy–Sp; T; woodland, hedgerows, gardens; fp. sallow, blackthorn, dock

28 **Least Yellow Underwing** *N. interjecta* Schawerda; Jy–Sp; loc. E, W, I; hedgerows, waste ground, sand hills; fp. various incl. grasses, primrose, dock

29 **Double Dart** *Graphiphora augur* Fabricius; J, Jy; loc. T; woodland, bushy areas; fp. hawthorn, birch, sallow

30 **Cousin German** *Paradiarsia sobrina* Duponchel; Jy, A; v. loc. S; birch woods; fp. bilberry, birch

PLATE 17: *Noctuidae*

Noctuidae (Noctuinae)

1 **Autumnal Rustic** *Paradiarsia glareosa* Esper; A, Sp; T; heathland, wood edges; fp. various incl. heather, sallow, dock

2 **True Lover's Knot** *Lycophotia porphyrea* Denis & Schiffermüller; J–Sp; T; heathland, moorland; fp. heather, bell heather

3 **Ingrailed Clay** *Diarsia mendica* Fabricius

4 **Ingrailed Clay** *Diarsia mendica* Fabricius; My–A; T; woodland, heathland; fp. various incl. sallow, hawthorn, heather

5 **Barred Chestnut** *D. dahlii* Hübner ♂

6 **Barred Chestnut** *D. dahlii* Hübner ♀; A, Sp; E (v. loc. in s), S, W, I; woodland, moorland; fp. birch, bilberry

7 **Purple Clay** *D. brunnea* D. & S.; J–A; T; woodland; fp. birch, sallow, dock, bilberry

8 **Pearly Underwing** *Peridroma saucia* Hb.; My–O; mig. T; waste ground, woodland, gardens; fp. various herbaceous plants incl. dock

9 **Small Square-spot** *Diarsia rubi* Vieweg; My, J, A, Sp (E, W, I), Jy, A (S); T; woodland, marshy areas, gardens; fp. incl. heather, dandelion, dock

10 **Fen Square-spot** *D. florida* Schmidt; J, Jy; e&nwE, W; fens, marshy areas; fp. unrecorded (in captivity – dock)

11 **Northern Dart** *Xestia alpicola* Humphreys & Westwood

12 **Northern Dart** *Xestia alpicola* Humphreys & Westwood; J–A; nE, S, wI; mountainsides above 450 m; fp. crowberry

13 **Setaceous Hebrew Character** *X. c-nigrum* Linnaeus; My–O; T; woodland, heathland, cultivated ground; fp. nettle, bilberry, creeping willow

14 **Triple-spotted Clay** *X. ditrapezium* D. & S.; J–A; T; woodland, parks; fp. sallow, birch, bramble

15 **Double Square-spot** *X. triangulum* Hufnagel; J, Jy; T; woodland; fp. hawthorn, blackthorn, birch

16 **Dotted Clay** *X. baja* D. & S.; Jy, A; T; woodland, heathland, fp. birch, bog myrtle, blackthorn

17 **Ashworth's Rustic** *X. ashworthii* Doubleday; J–A; nW; slate & limestone hills & mountains; fp. incl. rock-rose, heather, foxglove

18 **Square-spotted Clay** *X. rhomboidea* Esp.; A; v. loc. sE, W, w&cS; woodland; fp. birch, bramble

19 **Neglected Rustic** *X. castanea* Esp.

20 **Neglected Rustic** *X. castanea* f. *neglecta* Hb.; A, Sp; T; heathland, moorland; fp. heather, heaths

21 **Six-striped Rustic** *X. sexstrigata* Haworth; Jy, A; T; marshy areas, damp woodland; fp. incl. bramble, bluebell

22 **Square-spot Rustic** *X. xanthographa* D. & S.; Jy–Sp; T; wood edges, waste ground, gardens; fp. grasses, dock, plantain

23 **Heath Rustic** *X. agathina* Duponchel

24 **Heath Rustic** *X. agathina* Duponchel; A, Sp; T; heathland, moorland; fp. heather

25 **Green Arches** *Anaplectoides prasina* D. & S.; J, Jy; T; woodland; fp. sallow, honeysuckle, bilberry

28 **Great Brocade** *Eurois occulta* Linn.; Jy–S; res. S, mig. T; heathland, mountain moorland; fp. bog myrtle

Noctuidae (Hadeninae)

26 **Pale Shining Brown** *Polia bombycina* Hufn.; J, Jy; s&seE, loc. c&nE & nW; downland; fp. unrecorded (in captivity – dock)

27 **Silvery Arches** *P. hepatica* Clerck; J, Jy; T; woodland, heathland; fp. birch, bog myrtle

29 **Grey Arches** *P. nebulosa* Hufn.

30 **Grey Arches** *P. nebulosa* Hufn.; J, Jy; T; woodland; fp. birch, sallow, bramble

PLATE 18: *Noctuidae*

Noctuidae (Noctuinae)

1 **The Gothic** *Naenia typica* Linnaeus; J–A; T; waste ground, gardens, marshy areas; fp. incl. dock, dandelion, sallow

3 **Red Chestnut** *Cerastis rubricosa* Denis & Schiffermüller; M–My; T; woodland, wet moorland; fp. incl. sallow, groundsel, bedstraws

4 **White-marked** *C. leucographa* D. & S.; M, Ap; loc. s, swc&nE, sW; woodland; fp. unrecorded (in captivity – dock, sallow)

Noctuidae (Hadeninae)

2 **Bordered Gothic** *Heliophobus reticulata* Haworth; J, Jy; sE, sI; downland, rough ground, sea-cliffs; fp. unrecorded (in captivity – knotgrass)

5 **Beautiful Yellow Underwing** *Anarta myrtilli* Linn.; Ap–A (J, Jy in n); T; heathland, moorland; fp. heather, heath

6 **Small Dark Yellow Underwing** *A. cordigera* Thunberg; My, J; loc. Scottish Highlands; moorland between 200 & 600 m; fp. bearberry

7 **Broad-bordered White Underwing** *A. melanopa* Thunb.; My, J; loc. mountains neE & S; mountainsides above 600 m; fp. crowberry, bilberry, cowberry

8 **The Nutmeg** *Discestra trifolii* Hufnagel; My, J, A, Sp (in s), J & Jy (in n); T; (loc. S, I); waste ground, agricultural land; fp. goosefoot, orache

9 **Beautiful Brocade** *Lacanobia contigua* D. & S.; J, Jy; T; woodland, heathland, moorland; fp. incl. sallow, bog myrtle, oak

10 **The Shears** *Hada nana* Hufn.

11 **The Shears** *Hada nana* Hufn. (Scotland); My–Jy, occ. also A in s; T; woodland, moorland; fp. dandelion, hawk's-beard

12 **Dog's Tooth** *Lacanobia suasa* D. & S.

13 **Dog's Tooth** *Lacanobia suasa* ab. *dissimilis* Knoch; My–Sp in s, J & Jy in n; E, W, I, sS; waste ground, moorland, salt-marshes; fp. dock, plantain

14 **White Colon** *Sideridis albicolon* Hübner; My, J also Jy, A in s; E, W, eS, loc. I; heathland, coastal sand hills; fp. incl. goosefoot, sea bindweed

15 **Cabbage Moth** *Mamestra brassicae* Linn.; My–Sp; T; gardens, agricultural land; fp. various, esp. cultivated brassicas

16 **Dot Moth** *Melanchra persicariae* Linn.; J–A; E, W, I, sS; gardens, parks, roadsides; fp. various wild & garden plants

17 **Light Brocade** *Lacanobia w-latinum* Hufn.; My–Jy, E, W, sS; downland, rough ground, heathland; fp. broom, dyer's greenweed

18 **Pale-shouldered Brocade** *L. thalassina* Hufn.; My–Jy; T; woodland, moorland; fp. oak, broom, hawthorn

19 **Bright-line Brown-eye** *L. oleracea* Linn.; My–A; T; gardens, waste ground, salt-marshes; fp. various incl. goosefoot, tomato

20 **Broom Moth** *Ceramica pisi* Linn.; My–Jy; T; woodland, heathland, moorland; fp. various incl. bracken, broom, birch

21 **Glaucous Shears** *Papestra biren* Goeze; My, J; c&nE, W, S, I, v. loc. swE; moorland; fp. various incl. bog myrtle, heather, bilberry

22 **Broad-barred White** *Hecatera bicolorata* Hufn.; My–A; E, W, S to Inverness, loc. I; downland, waste ground; fp. hawkweed, hawk's-beard (flowers)

23 **The Campion** *Hadena rivularis* Fabricius; My, J also Jy & A in s; T; damp meadows, hedgerows, woodland; fp. campions, ragged robin (seeds)

24 **Tawny Shears** *H. perplexa* D. & S.

25 **Tawny Shears** *H. perplexa* D. & S.; My, J also A in s; E, W, sS; downland, chalky areas, shingle beaches; fp. white campion, sea campion (seeds)

26 **The Pod Lover** *H. perplexa capsophila* Duponchel; My, J; Isle of Man, I; shingle beaches, coastal areas; fp. sea campion, bladder campion (seeds)

27 **Viper's Bugloss** *H. irregularis* Hufn.; My–Jy; v. loc. East Anglia; roadsides, waste ground; fp. Spanish catchfly (seeds)

28 **Barrett's Marbled Coronet** *H. luteago* Doubleday; J, Jy; swE, n&sW, sI; coastal cliffs; fp. sea campion (roots)

29 **Varied Coronet** *H. compta* D. & S.; J, Jy; seE, East Anglia; gardens; fp. sweet william (seeds)

30 **Marbled Coronet** *H. confusa* Hufn.; My–Jy, also A in se; T; chalk downs, sea-cliffs; fp. bladder campion, sea campion (seeds)

31 **White Spot** *H. albimacula* Borkhausen; J, Jy; coastal v. loc. sE; shingle beaches, chalk cliffs; fp. Nottingham catchfly (seeds)

32 **The Lychnis** *H. bicruris* Hufn.; My–Jy, also A & Sp in s; T; woodland, gardens, roadsides, heathland; fp. red campion, white campion (seeds)

33 **The Grey** *H. caesia* Gregson; My–A; coastal loc. s&wI, Isle of Man, wS, Hebrides; sea-cliffs, rocky coastal areas; fp. sea campion (seeds)

34 **The Silurian** *Eriopygodes imbecilla* Fabr. ♂

35 **The Silurian** *Eriopygodes imbecilla* Fabr. ♀; J, Jy; v. loc. sW; mountainsides; fp. probably grasses (in captivity – withered dandelion)

36 **Antler Moth** *Cerapteryx graminis* Linn.; Jy–Sp; T; downland, grassy hillsides, moorland; fp. grasses, esp. mat-grass, sheep's-fescue

37 **Hedge Rustic** *Tholera cespitis* D. & S.; A, Sp; T except nS; grassy areas; fp. grasses, esp. mat-grass, hair grasses

38 **Pine Beauty** *Panolis flammea* D. & S.; M–My; T; pinewoods, parks; fp. pines

PLATE 19: *Noctuidae*

Noctuidae (Hadeninae)

1 **Feathered Gothic** *Tholera decimalis* Poda; A, Sp; E, W, I, loc. in S; downland, rough grassy areas; fp. grasses

2 **Silver Cloud** *Egira conspicillaris* f. *melaleuca* Vieweg; Ap, My; E (Severn Valley area); woodland, bushy areas; fp. unrecorded (in captivity – bird's-foot trefoil)

3 **Small Quaker** *Orthosia cruda* Denis & Schiffermüller; M, Ap; E, W, loc. S & I; woodland; fp. oak, sallow, hazel

4 **Blossom Underwing** *O. miniosa* D. & S.; M, Ap; E, W, loc. in I; woodland; fp. oak

5 **Northern Drab** *O, opima* Hübner

6 **Northern Drab** *O. opima* ab. *brunnea* Tutt; Ap, My; E, W, I, sS; downland, heathland, sand hills; fp. birch, sallow, ragwort

7 **Lead-coloured Drab** *O. populeti* Fabricius

8 **Lead-coloured Drab** *O. populeti* Fabricius; M, Ap; E, W, s&cS; woodland, parks; fp. aspen

9 **Powdered Quaker** *O. gracilis* D. & S.

10 **Powdered Quaker** *O. gracilis* D. & S. (bog myrtle race); Ap, My; T; heathland, moorland, woodland; fp. sallow, bog myrtle, yellow loosestrife

11 **Common Quaker** *O. stabilis* D. & S.

12 **Common Quaker** *O. stabilis* D. & S.; M–My; T; woodland; fp. oak, sallow, birch, hazel

13 **Clouded Drab** *O. incerta* Hufnagel

14 **Clouded Drab** *O. incerta* Hufnagel

15 **Clouded Drab** *O. incerta* Hufnagel; M–My; T; woodland; fp. trees & shrubs incl. oak, sallow

16 **Twin-spotted Quaker** *O. munda* D. & S.; M, Ap; E, W, loc. sS & I; woodland; fp. trees incl. oak, sallow, aspen

17 **Hebrew Character** *O. gothica* Linnaeus; M–My; T; most types of habitat; fp. many trees, shrubs, herbaceous plants

18 **Double Line** *Mythimna turca* Linn.; J, Jy; swE, s&cW, loc. seE & Cheshire & Lancs.; woodland; fp. grasses, esp. cock's-foot

19 **Brown-line Bright-eye** *M. conigera* D. & S.; J–A; T; woodland, roadsides; fp. grasses, esp. cock's-foot

20 **The Clay** *M. ferrago* Fabr.; J–A; T; woodland, heathland, roadsides; fp. grasses, dandelion

21 **White-point** *M. albipuncta* D. & S.; J–O; mig. s&seE; coastal areas; fp. grasses

22 **The Delicate** *M. vitellina* Hb.; My–N; mig. sE, W, sI; grassy coastal areas; fp. grasses

23 **Striped Wainscot** *M. pudorina* D. & S.; J, Jy; W, E to Yorks, swI; wet heathland, marshy areas; fp. common reed, hairy wood-rush, grasses

24 **Smoky Wainscot** *M. impura* Hb.; J–A, occ. also Sp, O in s; T; downland, rough ground, sand hills; fp. grasses

25 **Southern Wainscot** *M. straminea* Treitschke; Jy, A; E, W, sI; Reed-beds, ditches, marshy areas; fp. common reed, canary grass

26 **Common Wainscot** *M. pallens* Linn.

27 **Common Wainscot** *M. pallens* ab. *ectypa* Hb.; J–O (Jy–Sp in n); T; damp meadows, marshy areas; fp. grasses, esp. cock's-foot

28 **Shore Wainscot** *M. litoralis* Curtis; J–A; coastal T; coastal sand hills; fp. marram

29 **Mathew's Wainscot** *M. favicolor* Barrett

30 **Mathew's Wainscot** *M. favicolor* Barrett; J, Jy; seE; salt-marshes; fp. common salt-marsh grass

31 **L-album Wainscot** *M. l-album* Linn.; Jy, Sp, O; coastal sE; grassy areas; fp. grasses

32 **White-speck** *M. unipuncta* Haworth; J–O; mig. s&wE, W, swI; coastal areas; fp. grasses

33 **Obscure Wainscot** *M. obsoleta* Hb.; My–Jy; v. loc. se&cE; fens, marshy areas; fp. common reed

34 **Shoulder-striped Wainscot** *M. comma* Hb.; J, Jy; E, W, I, eS; fens, woodland, grassy areas; fp. grasses, esp. cock's-foot

35 **Devonshire Wainscot** *M. putrescens* Hb.; Jy, A; v. loc. swE, swW; sea-cliffs, coastal grassy areas; fp. grasses

36 **Flame Wainscot** *Senta flammea* Curtis; My–Jy; res. loc. East Anglia, mig. sE; reed-beds; fp. common reed

PLATE 20: *Noctuidae*

Noctuidae (Cucullinae)

1 **Chamomile Shark** *Cucullia chamomillae* Denis & Schiffermüller; Ap–J; E, W, I, S to Inverness; roadsides, waste ground, commons; fp. mayweeds, chamomiles

2 **The Shark** *C. umbratica* Linnaeus; J, Jy; T; waste ground, gardens, downland; fp. sow-thistles, wild lettuce

3 **Star-wort** *C. asteris* D. & S.; J–A; s&eE, n&sW; woodland, salt-marshes; fp. goldenrod, sea aster (flowers)

4 **Striped Lychnis** *C. lychnitis* Rambur; J, Jy; v. loc. sE; roadsides, chalk downs, waste ground; fp. dark mullein (flowers)

5 **The Mullein** *C. verbasci* Linn.; Ap, My; E, W, v. loc. sI; downland, waste ground, gardens; fp. mulleins, figworts, buddleia

6 **The Cudweed** *C. gnaphalii* Boursin; My–Jy; v. loc. seE; woodland clearings; fp. goldenrod (flowers & leaves)

7 **Toadflax Brocade** *Calophasia lunula* Hufnagel; My, J, A; seE; waste ground, gardens, shingle beaches; fp. common toadflax

8 **The Wormwood** *Cucullia absinthii* Linn.; Jy, A; s, c, e&nwE, W, sI; waste ground, commons, sea-cliffs; fp. wormwood, mugwort (flowers & seeds)

9 **The Sprawler** *Brachionycha sphinx* Hufn.; O–D; E, W, loc. in I; woodland; fp. trees incl. oak, sallow, hazel

10 **Rannoch Sprawler** *B. nubeculosa* Esper; M, Ap; loc. Inverness-shire, Rannoch; birch woods; fp. birch

11 **Feathered Brindle** *Aporophyla australis* Humphreys & Westwood; A–O; coastal s, se&swE, seI; downland, sea-cliffs, sand hills; fp. sea campion, grasses

12 **Minor Shoulder-knot** *Brachylomia viminalis* Fabricius

13 **Minor Shoulder-knot** *Brachylomia viminalis* Fabricius; Jy; A; E, W, S, loc. in I; woodland, marshy areas; fp. sallows, willows

14 **Beautiful Gothic** *Leucochlaena oditis* Hübner; A–O; v. loc. swE; sea-cliffs, grassy coastal slopes; fp. grasses

15 **Brindled Green** *Dryobotodes eremita* Fabr.; A, Sp; E, W, loc. in S & n&eI; woodland; fp. oak

16 **Black-banded** *Polymixis xanthomista* Gregson; A, Sp; coastal v. loc. swE, sW, sI; rocky areas; fp. thrift (flowers & leaves)

17 **Brindled Ochre** *Dasypolia templi* Thunberg; Sp, O, M, Ap; (hibernates); s, sw, c&nE, n&sW, S, loc. I; sea-cliffs, roadsides, mountain moorland; fp. hogweed, wild angelica (in stems & roots)

18 **Golden-rod Brindle** *Lithomoia solidaginis* Hb.; A, Sp; res. nE & nW & S, mig. seE; moorland, woodland; fp. incl. heather, birch, bog myrtle

19 **Tawny Pinion** *Lithophane semibrunnea* Haworth; O, N, M–My; (hibernates); s&cE, W; woodland; fp. ash

20 **Pale Pinion** *L. socia* Hufn.; O, N, M–My; (hibernates); s&cE, W, I, Isle of Man; woodland; fp. trees & shrubs, esp. sallow

21 **Deep-brown Dart** *Aporophyla lutulenta* D. & S.; Sp, O; s&eE; downland, waste ground, sea-cliffs; fp. grasses, hawthorn

22 **Northern Deep-brown Dart** *A. lueneburgensis* Freyer

23 **Northern Deep-brown Dart** *A. lueneburgensis* Freyer; A, Sp; nE, nW, n&wI, Isle of Man; moorland, grassy coastal areas; fp. heather, bird's-foot trefoil

24 **Early Grey** *Xylocampa areola* Esp.; M–My; T; (loc. S); woodland, hedgerows, gardens; fp. honeysuckle

25 **Black Rustic** *Aporophyla nigra* Haw. ♂

26 **Black Rustic** *Aporophyla nigra* Haw. ♀; Sp, O; E, W, S, coastal in I; heathland, downland, waste ground; fp. grasses, heather, bedstraws

27 **Grey Shoulder-knot** *Lithophane ornitopus* Dadd; Sp, O, F–Ap; (hibernates); s&cE, W, I; woodland, parks; fp. oak

28 **Blair's Shoulder-knot** *L. leautieri* Boursin; O, N; s&cE; gardens, parks; fp. Monterey cypress

29 **Red Sword-grass** *Xylena vetusta* Hb.; Sp, O, M, Ap; (hibernates); T (loc. eE); damp woodland, marshy areas, mountain moorland; fp. incl. dock, bog myrtle, yellow iris

30 **Sword-grass** *X. exsoleta* Linn.; Sp, O, M, Ap; (hibernates); nE, s&cW, S, nwI; woodland, moorland; fp. unrecorded (in captivity – dock)

31 **Merveille du Jour** *Dichonia aprilina* Linn.; Sp–N; E, W, nI, loc. S, woodland, parks; fp. oak

PLATE 21: *Noctuidae*

Noctuidae (Cucullinae)

1 **Green-brindled Crescent** *Allophyes oxyacanthae* Linnaeus
2 **Green-brindled Crescent** *Allophyes oxyacanthae* f. *capucina* Milliere; Sp–N; T; woodland, hedgerows, bushy areas; fp. hawthorn, blackthorn
3 **Dark Brocade** *Blepharita adusta* Esper
4 **Dark Brocade** *Blepharita adusta* Esper; My–A; T; chalk downs, heathland, fens; fp. grasses, bog myrtle
5 **Large Ranunculus** *Polymixis flavicincta* Denis & Schiffermüller; Sp, O; s, e&neE, sW; sea-cliffs, waste ground, gardens; fp. ragwort, delphinium, red valerian
6 **Grey Chi** *Antitype chi* Linn.
7 **Grey Chi** *Antitype chi* Linn.; A, Sp; E (loc. in s), W, S, nI; moorland, grassy hillsides; fp. dock, sorrel
8 **Feathered Ranunculus** *Eumichtis lichenea* Hübner; A–O, mainly coastal E, W, swS, eI; sea-cliffs, waste ground, gardens; fp. incl. red valerian, ragwort, sea plaintain
9 **The Satellite** *Eupsilia transversa* Hufnagel; Sp–Ap; T; woodland, parks; fp. trees incl. oak, sallow, birch
10 **Orange Upperwing** *Jodia croceago* D. & S.; Sp–N, M–My; (hibernates); v. loc. se&swE; woodland; fp. oak
11 **The Chestnut** *Conistra vaccinii* Linn.
12 **The Chestnut** *Conistra vaccinii* Linn.; Sp–My; T; woodland; fp. trees incl. oak, birch, willow
13 **Dark Chestnut** *C. ligula* Esp.
14 **Dark Chestnut** *C. ligula* f. *spadicea* Haworth; O–F; E, W, v. loc. sS & eI;

woodland, hedgerows; fp. oak, sallow, hawthorn
15 **Dotted Chestnut** *C. rubiginea* D. & S.; O, N, M, Ap; (hibernates); loc. s&swE, sW; woodland, heathland; fp. unrecorded (in captivity – blackthorn)
16 **The Brick** *Agrochola circellaris* Hufn.; Sp–N; T; woodland, parks; fp. wych elm (flowers & seeds), poplar
17 **Red-line Quaker** *A. lota* Clerck; Sp–N; T (loc. S); woodland, heathland, marshy areas; fp. sallow, willow
18 **Yellow-line Quaker** *A. macilenta* Hb.; Sp–N; T; woodland, bushy areas, moorland; fp. beech, oak, hawthorn, heather
19 **Flounced Chestnut** *A. helvola* Linn.; Sp, O; T (loc. S & nI); woodland, downland, moorland; fp. incl. oak, hawthorn, heather
20 **Brown-spot Pinion** *A. litura* Linn.; A–O; E, W, S; woodland, heathland, gardens; fp. incl. oak, hawthorn, chickweed, bramble
21 **Beaded Chestnut** *A. lychnidis* D. & S.
22 **Beaded Chestnut** *A. lychnidis* D. & S.; Sp–N; s&cE, W, I, loc. nE & S; woodland, bushy areas, waste ground; fp. grasses, hawthorn
23 **Lunar Underwing** *Omphaloscelis lunosa* Haw.
24 **Lunar Underwing** *Omphaloscelis lunosa* Haw.; A–O; E, W, I, loc. sS; downland, grassy areas; fp. grasses (leaves, stems, roots)
25 **The Suspected** *Parastichtis suspecta* Hb.; Jy, A; E, nW, S, loc. I; woodland, heathland; fp. birch, sallow
26 **Centre-barred Sallow** *Atethmia centrago* Haw.; A, Sp; E, W, S, loc. I; woodland, hedgerows; fp. ash
27 **Orange Sallow** *Xanthia citrago* Linn.;

A–O; T (loc. S); parks, roadsides, woodland; fp. lime
28 **Barred Sallow** *X. aurago* D. & S.; Sp, O; E, W; woodland, hedgerows; fp. field maple, beech
29 **The Sallow** *X. icteritia* Hufn.
30 **The Sallow** *X. icteritia* Hufn.; Sp. O; T; damp woodland, heathland, marshy areas; fp. sallow (catkins & leaves)
31 **Dusky-lemon Sallow** *X. gilvago* D. & S.; A–O; E, W, sS; woodland, commons; fp. wych elm, English elm (seeds)
32 **Pale-lemon Sallow** *X. ocellaris* Borkhausen; Sp, O; loc. seE; parks, roadsides, river valleys; fp. black poplar (catkins & seeds)
33 **Pink-barred Sallow** *X. togata* Esp.; Sp, O; T; damp woodland, marshy areas; fp. sallow (catkins)

Noctuidae (Acronictinae)

34 **Scarce Merveille du Jour** *Moma alpium* Osbeck; J, Jy; v. loc. seE; woodland; fp. oak
35 **Poplar Grey** *Acronicta megacephala* Denis & Schiffermüller
36 **Poplar Grey** *Acronicta megacephala* ab. *nigra* Shaw; My–A; E, W, loc. S & I; woodland, parks, gardens; fp. black poplar, aspen, willow
37 **Knot Grass** *A. rumicis* Linn.
38 **Knot Grass** *A. rumicis* ab. *salicis* Curtis; My–Jy, also A & Sp in s; T; woodland, rough ground, moorland, gardens; fp. incl. bramble, hawthorn, dock
39 **Light Knot Grass** *A. menyanthidis* Esp.
40 **Light Knot Grass** *A. menyanthidis* ab. *suffusa* Tutt; My–Jy; W, c&nE, S, nI; heathland, moorland, marshy areas; fp. heather, bog myrtle, birch, sallow

PLATE 22: *Noctuidae*

Noctuidae (Acronictinae)

1 **The Sycamore** *Acronicta aceris* Linnaeus
2 **The Sycamore** *Acronicta aceris* ab. *infuscata* Haworth; J–A; cs&seE, East Anglia, loc. sw&cE & W; parks, avenues, woodland; fp. horse chestnut, sycamore, field maple
3 **The Miller** *A. leporina* Linn.
4 **The Miller** *A. leporina* ab. *melanocephala* Mansbridge; J–A; E, W, loc. S & I; heathland, moorland, woodland; fp. birch, sallow, alder
5 **Alder Moth** *A. alni* Linn.; My–Jy; E, W, loc. I; woodland, commons; fp. birch, alder, hawthorn
6 **Dark Dagger** *A. tridens* Denis & Schiffermüller; J, Jy; E, W; woodland, orchards, gardens; fp. hawthorn, blackthorn, fruit trees
7 **Grey Dagger** *A. psi* Linn.; J–A; T; woodland, gardens, heathland; fp. hawthorn, blackthorn, oak, birch
8 **Sweet Gale Moth** *A. euphorbiae* Guenée; Ap–J, also A in I; c&nS, wI; moorland; fp. bog myrtle, heather, sallow
9 **Reed Dagger** *Simyra albovenosa* Goeze; My, Jy, A; v. loc. seE, East Anglia; fens, marshes, fp. common reed
10 **The Coronet** *Craniophora ligustri* D. & S.
11 **The Coronet** *Craniophora ligustri* ab. *coronula* Haw.; J–A; loc. E, W, S, wI; woodland, downland, commons; fp. ash, wild privet
13 **Marbled Beauty** *Cryphia domestica* Hufnagel; J–A, E, W, sS, v. loc. eS & I; coastal cliffs, urban areas, stone walls; fp. lichens on rocks, walls, roofs
14 **Marbled Green** *C. muralis* Forster

15 **Marbled Green** *C. muralis* Forster; Jy–Sp; loc. sE, sW, sI; rocky areas, stone walls; fp. lichens on rocks, walls

Noctuidae (Amphipyrinae)

12 **Mouse Moth** *Amphipyra tragopoginis* Clerck; Jy–Sp; T; woodland, moorland, gardens, marshy areas; fp. incl. hawthorn, sallow, chickweed
16 **Bird's Wing** *Dypterygia scabriuscula* Linn.; J, Jy, A, Sp; s&cE, W; woodland; fp. dock, sorrel
17 **Brown Rustic** *Rusina ferruginea* Esper; J, Jy; T; woodland, downland, heathland; fp. dock, groundsel, vetches
18 **Old Lady** *Mormo maura* Linn.; Jy, A; E, W, I, sS; river banks, gardens, marshy areas; fp. blackthorn, hawthorn, sallow
19 **Copper Underwing** *Amphipyra pyramidea* Linn.; Jy–O; s&cE, W, I, loc. nE & S; woodland, parks, hedgerows; fp. oak, ash, honeysuckle
20 **Svensson's Copper Underwing** *A. berbera* Fletcher; Jy–Sp; E, W, S; woodland, parks; fp. oak, sallow
21 **Straw Underwing** *Thalpophila matura* Hufn.; Jy, A; T; downland, moorland, grassy areas; fp. grasses
22 **Angle Shades** *Phlogophora meticulosa* Linn.; Ja–D; T; hedgerows, gardens, woodland, waste ground; fp. incl. dock, chickweed, bramble
23 **Small Angle Shades** *Euplexia lucipara* Linn.; J, Jy occ. Sp; T; woodland, parks, gardens; fp. bracken, wild & cultivated ferns, birch
24 **Angle-striped Sallow** *Enargia paleacea* Esp.; Jy–Sp; cE, cS; woodland; fp. birches
25 **Double Kidney** *Ipimorpha retusa*

Linn.; Jy–Sp; s&cE, W; damp woodland, marshy areas; fp. sallow, willow
26 **The Olive** *I. subtusa* D. & S.; Jy–Sp; E, W, sS, loc. I; woodland, parks, marshy areas; fp. poplar, aspen
27 **Lesser-spotted Pinion** *Cosmia affinis* Linn.; Jy, A; s&cE, W; woodland, hedgerows; fp. English elm, wych elm
28 **White-spotted Pinion** *C. diffinis* Linn.; Jy–Sp; loc. s&cE, W; woodland, hedgerows; fp. English elm, wych elm
29 **Lunar-spotted Pinion** *C. pyralina* D. & S.; Jy, A; s&cE, W; woodland, gardens, orchards; fp. English elm, wych elm, apple, hawthorn
30 **Dingy Shears** *Enargia ypsillon* D. & S.; J–A; E, W, loc. S & I; Damp woodland, marshy areas; fp. willow
31 **Heart Moth** *Dicycla oo* Linn.; J–A; v. loc. seE; woodland, parks; fp. oak
32 **The Dun-bar** *Cosmia trapezina* Linn.
33 **The Dun-bar** *Cosmia trapezina* Linn.; Jy–Sp; T; woodland, parks, hedgerows; fp. trees & shrubs incl. oak, birch, sallow
34 **The Saxon** *Hyppa rectilinea* Esp.; My–Jy; nE, S, swI; woodland, moorland; fp. sallow, bramble, bearberry
35 **Clouded-bordered Brindle** *Apamea crenata* Hufn.; My–Jy; T; woodland, downland, moorland; fp. grasses, esp. cock's-foot
36 **Clouded Brindle** *A. epomidion* Haw.; J, Jy; E, W, sS, loc. I; woodland, parks; fp. grasses
37 **The Confused** *A. furva* Cockayne; Jy, A; c&nE, Kent, W, S, loc. swE & I; rocky coastal areas, mountain moorland; fp. rough meadow-grass, wood meadow-grass (roots & stem bases)

PLATE 23: *Noctuidae*

Noctuidae (Amphipyrinae)

1 **Dark Arches** *Apamea monoglypha* Hufnagel; J–A, also A–O in s; T; grassy areas, agricultural land; fp. grasses, esp. cock's-foot (roots & stem bases)

2 **Light Arches** *A. lithoxylaea* Denis & Schiffermüller; J–A; T; grassy areas; fp. grasses

3 **The Exile** *A. maillardi* Lefebvre; Jy, A; Shetland; mountain & peat moorlands; fp. unrecorded (probably grasses)

4 **Reddish Light Arches** *A. sublustris* Esper; J, Jy; E, W, I; downland, rough grassy areas, breckland; fp. unrecorded (probably grasses)

5 **Northern Arches** *A. maillardi assimilis* Doubleday; Jy, A; S (Highlands), Orkney; mountain moorlands; fp. unrecorded (probably grasses)

6 **Crescent Striped** *A. oblonga* Haworth; J–A; coastal E (except sw), W; salt-marshes, river estuaries; fp. salt-marsh grass (roots & stem bases)

7 **Dusky Brocade** *A. remissa* f. *obscura* Haw.

8 **Dusky Brocade** *A. remissa* Hübner; J, Jy; T; downland, grassy areas, wood edges; fp. grasses

9 **Large Nutmeg** *A. anceps* D. & S.; J, Jy; s, c&neE, nW; downland, grassy areas, wood edges; fp. grasses

10 **Rustic Shoulder-knot** *A. sordens* Hufn.; My, J; T; meadows, grassy areas, roadsides; fp. grasses, esp. cock's-foot

11 **Small Clouded Brindle** *A. unanimis* Hb.; My–Jy; E, W, sS, nI; damp woodland, river valleys, marshy areas; fp. grasses

12 **Slender Brindle** *A. scolopacina* Esp.; J–A; E, W; woodland; fp. woodland grasses

13 **Double Lobed** *A. ophiogramma* Esp.; J–A; E, W, sS, nI; river banks, gardens, marshy areas; fp. reed canary-grass (inside stems)

14 **Marbled Minor** *Oligia strigilis* Linnaeus; My–Jy; E, W, S, loc. I; grassy areas, wood edges, downland; fp. grasses, esp. cock's-foot (inside stems)

15 **Rufous Minor** *O. versicolor* Borkhausen; J, Jy; E, W, sS, swI; grassy areas, woodland rides; fp. unrecorded

16 **Tawny Marbled Minor** *O. latruncula* D. & S.

17 **Tawny Marbled Minor** *O. latruncula* f. *unicolor* Tutt; My–Jy; grassy areas, woodland rides; fp. grasses (inside stems)

18 **Cloaked Minor** *Mesoligia furuncula* D. & S.

19 **Cloaked Minor** *Mesoligia furuncula* D. & S.; Jy–Sp; T; grassy areas, downland, sea-cliffs; fp. grasses (inside stems)

20 **Middle-barred Minor** *Oligia fasciuncula* Haw.; J, Jy; T; damp grassy areas, river banks; fp. grasses (leaves)

21 **Rosy Minor** *Mesoligia literosa* Haw.

22 **Rosy Minor** *Mesoligia literosa* f. *aethalodes* Richardson; Jy, A; T; grassy areas, chalk sea-cliffs, waste ground; fp. grasses (inside stems & roots)

23 **Least Minor** *Photedes captiuncula* Stainton; J–A; loc. nE, wI; limestone hills, grassy sea-cliffs; fp. glaucous sedge (inside stems)

24 **Common Rustic** *Mesapamea secalis* Linn.

25 **Common Rustic** *Mesapamea secalis* Linn.; Jy–Sp; T; grassy areas, woodland rides, downland; fp. grasses (inside stems)

26 **Lesser Common Rustic** *M. secalella* Remm; Jy, A; T; grassy areas, woodland rides, downland; fp. unrecorded (probably grasses)

27 **Small Dotted Buff** *Photedes minima* Haw. ♂

28 **Small Dotted Buff** *Photedes minima* Haw. ♀; J–A; T; damp woodland & meadows, marshy areas; fp. tufted hair-grass (inside stems)

29 **Morris's Wainscot** *P. morrisii* Dale; J, Jy; v. loc. swE, Kent; grassy coastal slopes, undercliffs; fp. tall fescue (inside stems)

30 **The Concolorous** *P. extrema* Hb.; J. Jy; v. loc. Hunts., Northants., Lincs.; fenland, marshy woodland; fp. purple small-reed (inside stems)

31 **Lyme Grass** *P. elymi* Treit

32 **Lyme Grass** *P. elymi* Treit; J–A; coastal, loc. eE, eS; sand hills; fp. lyme-grass (inside lower stems)

33 **Mere Wainscot** *P. fluxa* Hb.

34 **Mere Wainscot** *P. fluxa* Hb.; Jy, A; s, c&eE; fen margins, damp woodland, marshy areas; fp. wood small-reed (inside stems)

35 **Fenn's Wainscot** *P. brevilinea* Fenn; Jy, A; loc. East Anglia; fenland reed-beds; fp. common reed (inside stems)

36 **Small Wainscot** *P. pygmina* Haw.

37 **Small Wainscot** *P. pygmina* Haw.; A, Sp; T; damp woodland, moorland, marshy areas; fp. sedges, rushes (inside stems)

38 **Dusky Sallow** *Eremobia ochroleuca* D. & S.; Jy, A; cs, se&eE; downland, waste ground, grassy areas; fp. grasses (flowers & seeds)

39 **Flounced Rustic** *Luperina testacea* D. & S.

40 **Flounced Rustic** *Luperina testacea* D. & S.; A, Sp; E, W, loc. S, coastal I; downland, coastal cliffs, grassy areas; fp. grasses (roots & stem bases)

41 **Sandhill Rustic** *L. nickerlii gueneei* Doubleday; Jy–Sp; coastal nW, Lancs; sand hills; fp. sand couch (root crowns & stem bases)

42 **Ear Moth** *Amphipoea oculea* Linn.; Jy–Sp; T; damp meadows & woodland, marshy areas; fp. grasses, butterbur (roots & stem bases)

43 **Saltern Ear** *A. fucosa* Tutt; A, Sp; coastal E, W, S; salt-marshes, sand hills, wet moorland; fp. grasses (roots & stem bases)

44 **Crinan Ear** *A. crinanensis* Burrows; A, Sp; nE, wW, S, I; wet meadows & stream banks, moorland; fp. yellow iris (inside stems)

PLATE 24: *Noctuidae*

Noctuidae (Amphipyrinae)

1 **Large Ear** *Amphipoea lucens* Freyer; A, Sp; w, c&nE, W, S, coastal in I; wet moorland, mosses; fp. purple moor-grass (in roots & stem bases)

2 **The Butterbur** *Hydraecia petasitis* Doubleday; A, Sp; E, W, sS; riversides, marshy areas; fp. butterbur (inside stems & roots)

3 **Fisher's Estuarine Moth** *Gortyna borelii lunata* Freyer; Sp, O; v. loc. Essex; marshy meadows, waste ground; fp. hog's fennel (inside stems & roots)

4 **Rosy Rustic** *Hydraecia micacea* Esper; A–O; T; waste ground, gardens, fp. dock, plantain, tomato (in roots)

5 **Marsh Mallow Moth** *H. osseola hucherardi* Mabille; A–O; Kent, East Sussex; river banks, marshy areas; fp. marsh mallow (in roots)

6 **Frosted Orange** *Gortyna flavago* Denis & Schiffermüller; A–O; E, W, I, S to Moray; roadsides, waste ground, woodland; fp. thistles, foxglove, burdock (in stems)

7 **Burren Green** *Calamia tridens occidentalis* Cockayne; Jy, A; I (the Burren); limestone; fp. grasses (in stems & roots)

8 **The Crescent** *Celaena leucostigma* Hübner; Jy–Sp; loc. T; damp woodland, fens, marshy areas; fp. yellow iris, great fen-sedge (in stems & roots)

9 **Haworth's Minor** *C. haworthii* Curtis; A, Sp; c&nE, nW, S, I, loc. sw&csE & East Anglia & sW; wet moorland, fens, marshy areas; fp. cotton-grass (in stems)

10 **Twin-spotted Wainscot** *Archanara geminipuncta* Haworth

11 **Twin-spotted Wainscot** *Archanara geminipuncta* Haworth; A, Sp; s&seE, sW; reed-beds; fp. common reed (in stems)

12 **Brown-veined Wainscot** *A. dissoluta* f. *arundineta* Schmidt; Jy–Sp; s, e&cE, W; reed-beds; fp. common reed (in stems)

13 **Bulrush Wainscot** *Nonagria typhae* Thunberg ♂

14 **Bulrush Wainscot** *Nonagria typhae* Thunberg ♀

15 **Bulrush Wainscot** *Nonagria typhae* ab. *fraterna* Treitschke; A, Sp; E, W, I, s&sS; ponds, marshy areas, fens, ditches; fp. bulrush (in stems)

16 **Webb's Wainscot** *Archanara sparganii* Esp.

17 **Webb's Wainscot** *Archanara sparganii* Esp.; A–O; s&seE; v. loc. sW & sI; ponds, marshy areas, fens, ditches; fp. bulrush, yellow iris (in stems)

18 **Large Wainscot** *Rhizedra lutosa* Hb.; A–O; E, W, I, loc. S; reed-beds, riversides; fp. common reed (in roots & stem bases)

19 **Brighton Wainscot** *Oria musculosa* Hb.; Jy, A; csE; cereal fields; fp. grasses, cereals (in stems)

20 **White-mantled Wainscot** *Archanara neurica* Hb.; Jy, A; coastal v. loc. Suffolk; reed-beds; fp. common reed (in stems)

21 **Rush Wainscot** *A. algae* Esp.

22 **Rush Wainscot** *A. algae* Esp.; A, Sp; v. loc. e&seE & I; ponds, broadland; fp. common club-rush, yellow iris (in stems)

23 **Fen Wainscot** *Arenostola phragmitidis* Hb.; Jy, A; s, e&nwE; reed-beds; fp. common reed (in stems)

24 **Small Rufous** *Coenobia rufa* Haw.; Jy, A; E, W, sS, v. loc. swI; marshy areas, fens, bogs; fp. jointed rush (in stems)

25 **Treble Lines** *Charanyca trigrammica* Hufnagel

26 **Treble Lines** *Charanyca trigrammica* ab. *bilinea* Haw.; My–Jy; E, W, I, Isle of Man; woodland, downland, hedgerows; fp. incl. greater plantain, common knapweed

27 **The Uncertain** *Hoplodrina alsines* Brahm; J–A; T; waste ground, hedgerows, gardens; fp. dock, dandelion, plantain

28 **Mottled Rustic** *Caradrina morpheus* Hufn.; J–A, occ. O in s; E, W, S, v. loc. I; woodland, downland, gardens; fp. dandelion, nettle, chickweed

29 **The Rustic** *Hoplodrina blanda* D. & S.

30 **The Rustic** *Hoplodrina blanda* D. & S.; J–A; E, W, I, loc. S; downland, waste ground, gardens; fp. plantain, chickweed, dock

31 **Vine's Rustic** *H. ambigua* D. & S.; My–O; sE, East Anglia, loc. res. E, W, S, sI; heathland, waste ground, gardens; fp. dandelion, chickweed

32 **Small Mottled Willow** *Spodoptera exigua* Hb.; J–O; mig. T; fp. unrecorded (in captivity – dandelion)

33 **Pale Mottled Willow** *Caradrina clavipalpis* Scopoli; F–N; T; cultivated fields, gardens, waste ground; fp. cereals, peas, plantains (seeds)

34 **Marsh Moth** *Athetis pallustris* Hb. ♂

35 **Marsh Moth** *Athetis pallustris* Hb. ♀; My, J; v. loc. Hunts., Cambs., Lincs., Norfolk; fenland, marshy coastal areas; fp. meadowsweet

36 **Reddish Buff** *Acosmetia caliginosa* Hb. ♂

37 **Reddish Buff** *Acosmetia caliginosa* Hb. ♀; My, J; v. loc. northern Isle of Wight; woodland clearings; fp. saw-wort

38 **Silky Wainscot** *Chilodes maritimus* Tauscher; J–A; s&eE, sW; reed-beds; fp. common reed (in dead stems)

PLATE 25: *Noctuidae*

Noctuidae (Amphipyrinae)

1 **The Anomalous** *Stilbia anomala* Haworth ♂

2 **The Anomalous** *Stilbia anomala* Haworth ♀; A, Sp; s, c&nE, W, S, n&wI, Isle of Man; heathland, moorland; fp. wavy hair-grass

3 **Rosy Marbled** *Elaphria venustula* Hübner; My–Jy; loc. seE; woodland; fp. unrecorded (in captivity – tormentil flowers)

4 **Small Yellow Underwing** *Panemeria tenebrata* Scopoli; My, J; E, W, eS; downland, grassy areas; fp. common mouse-ear (seeds)

Noctuidae (Acontiinae)

5 **Silver Hook** *Eustrotia uncula* Clerck; My–Jy; E, W, I, wS; boggy heathland, fens, marshes; fp. cotton-grasses

6 **Silver Barred** *Deltote bankiana* Fabricius; J, Jy; res. Cambs., Kent & swI; mig. seE; boggy heathland, fens, marshes; fp. fenland grasses incl. purple moor-grass

17 **Marbled White Spot** *Lithacodia pygarga* Hufnagel; My–Jy; s&cE, W, swI; woodland, heathland, commons; fp. grasses incl. purple moor-grass

Noctuidae (Heliothinae)

7 **Bordered Sallow** *Pyrrhia umbra* Hufn.; J, Jy; E, W, S, I; downland, coastal sand hills, shingle beaches; fp. restharrows (leaves, flowers, & seeds)

8 **Scarce Bordered Straw** *Heliothis armigera* Hb.; J–O; mig. sE; fp. garden flowers, often in imported fruit.

9 **Bordered Straw** *H. peltigera* Denis & Schiffermüller; J–A; mig. s&seE; fp. garden marigold, heath groundsel (flowers)

10 **Marbled Clover** *H. viriplaca* Hufn.; J–A; res. East Anglia, mig. s&eE, chalk downs, clover fields, waste ground; fp. clovers, campions, restharrow (flowers & seeds)

11 **Shoulder-striped Clover** *H. maritima warneckei* Boursin; J, Jy; loc. Dorset, Hants., Surrey; damp heathland; fp. cross-leaved heath (flowers)

Noctuidae (Chloephorinae)

12 **Scarce Silver-lines** *Bena prasinana* Linnaeus; J–A; E, W; woodland, parks; fp. oak

13 **Green Silver-lines** *Pseudoips fagana* Warren; My–Jy, occ. A & Sp; E, W, loc. sS & I; woodland; fp. oak, beech, hazel, birch

14 **Cream-bordered Green Pea** *Earias clorana* Linn.; My–Jy, occ. A; s&eE, sI; damp woodland, river valleys, marshy areas; fp. willows, esp. osier

Noctuidae (Sarrothripinae)

15 **Oak Nycteoline** *Nycteola revayana* Scop.

16 **Oak Nycteoline** *Nycteola revayana* Scop.; Sp–N, M–My; (hibernates); s&cE, W, I, loc. nE & S; woodland; fp. oak

Noctuidae (Pantheinae)

18 **Nut-tree Tussock** *Colocasia coryli* Linn.; Ap–J, Jy, A; T; woodland, hedgerows; fp. hazel, beech, birch, field maple

Noctuidae (Plusiinae)

19 **The Ni Moth** *Trichoplusia ni* Hb.; My–O; mig. sE; fp. sea rocket, marigold

20 **Burnished Brass** *Diachrysia chrysitis* Linn.; J, Jy, A, Sp in s, Jy, A in n; T; waste ground, gardens, hedgerows; fp. common nettle

21 **Scarce Burnished Brass** *D. chryson* Esper; Jy, A; v. loc. csE, swW; river valleys, ditches, marshy areas; fp. hemp-agrimony

22 **Golden Plusia** *Polychrysia moneta* Fabr.; J–A, occ. also Sp in s; E, W, sS, Co. Dublin; gardens; fp. cultivated delphiniums, monk's-hood

23 **Gold Spot** *Plusia festucae* Linn.; J, Jy, A, Sp in s, J–A in n; T; river banks, boggy moorland, marshy areas; fp. yellow iris, marshland grasses

24 **Lempke's Gold Spot** *P. putnami gracilis* Lempke; Jy, A; East Anglia, nE, sS; marshy areas, fens, gardens; fp. unrecorded

25 **Silver Y** *Autographa gamma* Linn.; My–O; mig. T; any type of habitat; fp. most low-growing plants

26 **Scarce Silver Y** *Syngrapha interrogationis* Linn.; J–A; c&nE, W, S, I; moorland; fp. heather, bilberry

27 **Beautiful Golden Y** *Autographa pulchrina* Haw.; J, Jy; T; woodland, hedgerows, gardens; fp. dead-nettle, honeysuckle

28 **Plain Golden Y** *A. jota* Linn.; J–A; T; woodland, hedgerows, gardens; fp. dead-nettle, common nettle, honeysuckle

29 **Gold Spangle** *A bractea* D. & S.; Jy, A; c&nE, W, S, I, Isle of Man; roadsides, waste ground, woodland; fp. common nettle, dandelion

30 **Dark Spectacle** *Abrostola trigemina* Werneburg; J, Jy, occ. A, Sp; E, W, I, Isle of Man, loc. S; waste ground, hedgerows, gardens; fp. common nettle, hop

31 **The Spectacle** *A. triplasia* Linn.; My–Jy, occ. Jy–Sp in s; T; waste ground, woodland, gardens; fp. common nettle

Noctuidae (Catocalinae)

32 **Mother Shipton** *Callistege mi* Cl.; My, J; E, W, I. loc. S; downland, meadows, waste ground; fp. clovers, lucerne

33 **Burnet Companion** *Euclidia glyphica* Linn.; My, J; E, W, I, sS, Isle of Man; downland, damp meadows, wood edges; fp. clovers, lucerne, trefoils

Noctuidae (Ophiderinae)

34 **The Four-spotted** *Tyta luctuosa* D. & S.; My–A; v. loc. s&seE; chalk downs, waste ground; fp. field bindweed

35 **Small Purple-barred** *Phytometra viridaria* Cl.; My–Jy; T; chalk downs, heathland, woodland rides; fp. common milkwort

36 **Lesser Belle** *Colobochyla salicalis* D. & S.; J, Jy; v. loc. Kent; woodland; fp. aspen

37 **Beautiful Hook-tip** *Laspeyria flexula* D. & S.; J–A; s, se&cE, sW; woodland, orchards; fp. lichens on trees

PLATE 26: *Noctuidae*

Noctuidae (Catocalinae)

1 **Clifden Nonpareil** *Catocala fraxini* Linnaeus; Sp; mig. s&eE; woodland; fp. aspen, poplar

2 **Light Crimson Underwing** *C. promissa* Denis & Schiffermüller; Jy, A; seE; woodland; fp. oak

3 **Red Underwing** *C. nupta* Linn.; A, Sp; s, c&eE, W; woodland, parks, river valleys; fp. willow, poplar, aspen

4 **Dark Crimson Underwing** *C. sponsa* Linn.; A, Sp; v. loc. Hants.; woodland; fp. oak

Noctuidae (Ophiderinae)

5 **The Blackneck** *Lygephila pastinum* Treitschke; J, Jy; s&cE, East Anglia, sW; downland, wood edges, marshy areas; fp. tufted vetch

6 **Scarce Blackneck** *L. craccae* D. & S.; Jy, A; coastal v. loc. n. Devon, n. Cornwall; rocky coasts, sea-cliffs; fp. wood vetch

7 **The Herald** *Scoliopteryx libatrix* Linn.; Jy–N, M–J; (hibernates); T; woodland, hedgerows, gardens; fp. sallow, willow, poplar

8 **Straw Dot** *Rivula sericealis* Scopoli; My–Sp; E, W, wS, I, Isle of Man; damp woodland, damp heaths, marshes; fp. grasses

9 **Waved Black** *Parascotia fuliginaria* Linn.; J–A; seE, sW; damp woodland & heathland; fp. fungi on tree stumps & fallen timber

Noctuidae (Hypeninae)

10 **Olive Crescent** *Trisateles emortualis* D. & S.; J, Jy; loc. seE; woodland; fp. oak, beech (withered leaves)

11 **Beautiful Snout** *Hypena crassalis* Fabricius ♀

12 **Beautiful Snout** *Hypena crassalis* Fabricius ♂; My–Jy; s, wc&neE, W, sI; woodland; fp. bilberry

13 **The Snout** *H. proboscidalis* Linn.; J, Jy, Sp in s, Jy, A in n; T; woodland, hedgerows, waste ground, gardens; fp. common nettle

14 **Buttoned Snout** *H. rostralis* Linn.

15 **Buttoned Snout** *H. rostralis* Linn.; A–O, Ap–J; (hibernates); seE; hedgerows, bushy areas; fp. hop

16 **White-line Snout** *Schrankia taenialis* Hübner; Jy, A; sE, sW; damp woodland, heathland; fp. unrecorded

17 **Pinion-streaked Snout** *S.*

costaestrigalis Stephens; J–A, also Sp & O in s; E, W, S, loc. I; damp woodland, wet heathland, mosses; fp. unrecorded

18 **Marsh Oblique-barred** *Hypenodes humidalis* Doubleday; J–A, occ. Sp; loc. E, W, S, swI; boggy heathland & moorland; fp. unrecorded

19 **Common Fan-foot** *Pechipogo strigilata* Linn.; My, J; v. loc. seE; woodland; fp. withered leaves

20 **The Fan-foot** *Herminia tarsipennalis* Treit; J, Jy; T; woodland, hedgerows, gardens; fp. beech, oak, bramble (withered leaves)

21 **Shaded Fan-foot** *H. tarsicrinalis* Knoch; J, Jy; loc. East Anglia; woodland, bramble thickets; fp. withered leaves

22 **Small Fan-foot** *H. nemoralis* Fabr.; J–A; T; woodland, bushy areas, gardens; fp. oak, alder (live or withered leaves)

23 **Dotted Fan-foot** *Macrochilo cribrumalis* Hb.; J–A; v. loc. seE, East Anglia; fens, marshes; fp. marsh grasses, sedges

24 **Clay Fan-foot** *Paracolax derivalis* Hb.; J–A; loc. seE; woodland; fp. oak (fallen leaves)

Glossary

Abdomen Third major division of the body

Aberration A moth which differs in appearance from the normal

Aestivate To remain dormant during the summer

Anal tuft A prominent tuft of hairs on the tip of a moth's abdomen

Antennae A pair of sensory organs on the head

Apex The tip of the forewing

Basal Refers to the area of the wing closest to the body

Chorion The eggshell

Confluent Running together

Costa Front margin of the wing

Cremaster A device, often bearing hooks or spines, on the last segment of the pupa, enabling it to attach itself to a silken pad

Crenate Scalloped

Crest A prominent tuft of hairs on the dorsal surface of either the thorax or abdomen of the adult moth

Cryptic coloration Camouflage colouring which closely resembles bark, twigs, etc.

Dimorphic Occurs in two distinct forms

Discal spot A mark in the central area of the wing

Dorsal Upper surface

Dorsum Posterior (inner) margin of the wing

Eversible Capable of being turned inside-out

Form (f.) A variety

Frass Larval faeces

Frenulum Wing-coupling apparatus

Fringe The edging of scales or hairs round the termen

Fusiform Tapering gradually to each end

Girt Supported by a silken girdle round the thorax

Glabrous Hairless

Gynandromorph A moth exhibiting both male and female colour and/or markings

Haustellum Proboscis

Hemispherical Having the shape of half a sphere

Hibernaculum A shelter of leaves or other material spun together with silk in which a larva hibernates

Hyaline Transparent; lacking scales

Imago (pl. imagines) The adult moth

Inner margin Dorsum

Instar The period between two larval moults

Jugum Wing-coupling apparatus in Hepialidae

Lateral On the sides

Local Refers to populations where colonies are confined to a relatively small area

Mandibles Jaws

Melanic Suffused with black

Mesothorax Middle (second) segment of the thorax

Metathorax Rear (third) segment of the thorax

Micropyle The tiny opening in the eggshell through which sperm passes to fertilise the egg

Mimicry The resemblance of one individual to another, especially one of a different species

Mosaic A moth with patchy characteristics of the opposite sex

Orbicular stigma A round or oval mark in the cell area of the wing

Outer margin Termen

Ovipositor A tubular structure with which the eggs are inserted into crevices etc.

Palpi Sensory organs on the front of the head

Patagium (pl. patagia) Hairy pad on the prothorax of the adult moth

Pheromone A scent attractive to other individuals of the same species, usually of the opposite sex

Polyphagous Will eat a tremendous range of foodplants

Proboscis The tubular tongue of the moth

Prolegs The fleshy abdominal legs of the larva

Prothoracic plate A horny plate on the first thoracic segment

Prothorax Front (first) segment of the thorax

Reniform stigma Kidney-shaped mark at the

end of the cell on the forewing

Reticulated Bearing a net-work pattern

Retinaculum Part of the frenulum

Setae Stiff hairs or bristles

Sexually dimorphic The sexes are markedly different in appearance

sp. (pl. spp.) Species

Spinnerets Tubes from which silk is extruded by the larva

Spiracles The external openings of the tracheae

Spiracular In the region of the spiracles

ssp. Subspecies

Striations Fine short transverse lines

Subdorsal Below the dorsal line

Subspiracular Below the spiracles

Tegulae A pair of hairy pads on the mesothorax of the adult moth, behind the patagium

Termen The outer margin of the wing

Thorax Second major division

of the body, bearing the legs and wings

Tornus Junction of the termen and the dorsum

Tracheae Respiratory tubes

Tubercle A small projection on the skin of a larva which often bears hairs

Urticating Producing a skin rash similar to that caused by stinging nettles

Ventral Lower surface

♂ Male

♀ Female

Further Reading

Agassiz, D. et al., *An Identification Guide to the British Pugs*, British Entomological & Natural History Society, London, 1981

Allan, P. B. M., *Larval Foodplants*, Watkins & Doncaster, Kent, 1949

Buckler, W., *The Larvae of British Butterflies and Moths*, Vols 2–9, Ray Society, London, 1887–1901

Dickson, R., *A Lepidopterist's Handbook*, Amateur Entomologist's Society, London, 1976

Haggett, G. M., *Larvae of the British Lepidoptera not figured by Buckler*, British Entomological & Natural History Society, London, 1981

Heath, J. et al., *The Moths and Butterflies of Great Britain and Ireland*, Vols 1, 2, 7, 9, 10 (others to follow), Harley Books, Essex, 1976–

Scorer, A. G., *The Entomologist's Log-book*, Routledge & Sons, London, 1913

Skinner, B., *Colour Identification Guide to Moths of the British Isles*, Viking, Middlesex, 1984

South, R., *The Moths of the British Isles* (Vols 1 & 2), Warne, London, 1961

Stokoe, W. J., *The Caterpillars of the British Moths* (Vols 1 & 2), Warne, London, 1958

Tutt, J. W., *Practical Hints for the Field Lepidopterist* (Parts i–iii), Elliot Stock, London, 1908

Index

Italic numerals indicate pages where illustrations accompany the text
Bold numerals refer to plates in the section between pages 187 and 239